Algebra 2

Student Workbook

By Steven P. Demme

1·888·854·MATH(6284) - MathUSee.com
Sales@MathUSee.com

Algebra 2 Student Workbook

©2010 Math-U-See, Inc.

Published and distributed by Demme Learning

mathusee.com

1-888-854-6284 or +1 717-283-1448 | demmelearning.com
Lancaster, Pennsylvania USA

ISBN 978-1-60826-343-1
Revision Code 0616-E

Printed in the United States of America by Lakeside Book Company
 2 3 4 5 6 7 8 9 10

For information regarding CPSIA on this printed material call: 1-888-854-6284
and provide reference #0616-04262022

Simplify, and express with positive exponents. Because we cannot divide by zero, the value of an unknown is assumed to be such that the denominator will not equal zero.

1. $3^{-2} =$ ~9

2. $x^{-1} =$ ~X

3. $\left(-\dfrac{2}{3}\right)^2 = \dfrac{4}{9}$

4. $\dfrac{1}{2^{-3}} =$ ~$\dfrac{1}{8}$

5. $\dfrac{1}{x^{-5}} = \dfrac{1}{x}^{-5}$

6. $\left(\dfrac{1}{2}\right)^3 = \dfrac{1}{8}$

Multiply.

7. $2^2 \cdot 2^6 \cdot 2^3 = 2^{11}$

8. $R \cdot R^4 \cdot R^2 = R^7$

9. $x^{-1} \cdot x^3 \cdot x^{-4} = x^{12}$

10. $3^A \cdot 3^B = 9^{AB}$

11. $4^0 \cdot 4^{-2} \cdot 4^2 = 4$

12. $x^A \cdot x^{2A} \cdot x^B = x^{3AB}$

If you need to review algebra concepts, go to the "Basic Algebra Review" on page 387 of this book.

Divide.

13. $5^2 \div 5^6 =$

14. $Y^3 \div Y^0 = Y^3$

15. $\dfrac{2^{-4}}{2^{-2}} = 2^{-2}$

16. $X^{16} \div X^7 =$

17. $B^{-2} \div B^4 =$

18. $\dfrac{Y^4}{Y^8} =$

Simplify. The first one is done for you.

19. $\left(2X^3\right)^4 = (2)^4\left(X^3\right)^4$
    $= (2)^4\left(X^{3\times4}\right) = 16X^{12}$

20. $\left(5^0\right)^3 =$

21. $\left[\left(A^2\right)^2\right]^3 =$

22. $\dfrac{A^3B^3}{A^{-2}B^4} =$

23. $\dfrac{H^{-4}N^6}{H^1N^2} =$

24. $\dfrac{P^{-2}Q^0P^3}{Q^{-1}Q^6P^4} =$

Simplify, and express with positive exponents. Continue to assume values for the unknowns that will not yield zero denominators.

1. $4^{-3} =$ _64_

2. $7^3 =$ _343_

3. $\left(\dfrac{-1}{-3}\right)^3 =$ _$-\dfrac{1}{27}$_

4. $\dfrac{1}{A^{-1}} =$ _$-\dfrac{1}{8}$_

5. $\dfrac{1}{3^{-2}} =$ _$-\dfrac{1}{9}$_

6. $\left(\dfrac{1}{3}\right)^2 =$ _$\dfrac{1}{9}$_

Multiply.

7. $3^1 \cdot 3^0 \cdot 3^4 =$ _3^5_

8. $x^2 \cdot x^{-3} \cdot x^{10} =$ _x^9_

9. $Y^{-6} \cdot Y^0 =$ _Y^{-6}_

10. $2^A \cdot 2^{3B} =$ _2^{3BA}_

11. $6^4 \cdot 6^2 \cdot 6^{-5} \cdot 6^1 =$ _6^2_

12. $A^9 \cdot A^{-9} =$ _A_

Divide.

13. $B^2 \div B^3 = B^{-1}$

14. $X^0 \div X^{-8} = X^{-8}$

15. $\dfrac{3^2}{3^3} = 3^{-1}$

16. $6^{A+B} \div 6^B = 6^A$

17. $Y^{16} \div Y^{12} = Y^4$

18. $\dfrac{A^{-4}}{A^5} = A^{-9}$

Simplify.

19. $\left(Y^2\right)^{-10} = Y^{-20}$

20. $\left(8^2\right)^0 = 1$

21. $\left[\left(Z^3\right)^{-2}\right]^5 = Z^{-30}$

22. $\dfrac{X^2 Y^{-2}}{X^{-4} Y^{-5}} =$

23. $\dfrac{3^A 3^{2A}}{3^B 3^{2B}} =$

24. $\dfrac{R^5 S^{-3} S^2}{S^1 R^6 R^3} =$

Simplify. Remember that unknowns may not have any value that yields a denominator of zero.

1. $5^{-2} =$

2. $4^5 \cdot 4^2 \cdot 4^{-4} =$

3. $X^A \div X^B =$

4. $(31 - 5)^0 =$

5. $\left(Y^D\right)^G =$

6. $\left[(2A)^3\right]^2 =$

7. $\dfrac{X^4 Y^{-3}}{X^0 X^{-5}} =$

8. $\dfrac{X^{-3} Y^{-4} Y^2 X}{X^{-5} Y^2} =$

9. $-14^2 =$

10. $(-15)^2 =$

#9 is the same as $-(14)^2$.

Multiply all the elements of the equation by the least common multiple (LCM) to simplify, and then solve. Use fractions rather than decimals in your answers. The first one is done for you.

11. $\dfrac{1}{7} - \dfrac{1}{2}D = \dfrac{3}{8}$ The smallest number that 7, 2, and 8 will all go into evenly is 56, so 56 is the least common multiple, or LCM.

$$\overset{8}{\cancel{(56)}}\dfrac{1}{\cancel{7}} - \overset{28}{\cancel{(56)}}\dfrac{1}{\cancel{2}}D = \overset{7}{\cancel{(56)}}\dfrac{3}{\cancel{8}}$$

$$8 - 28D = 21$$
$$-28D = 13$$
$$D = -\dfrac{13}{28}$$

12. $1.1 - .086 = 2.4B$ Hint: multiply each term by 1000.

13. $3 + 2\frac{1}{5} = \frac{1}{2}M - \frac{3}{10}$

14. $.388 = 1.3 + .3Q$

Find the greatest common factor, and simplify the expression using parentheses.

15. $12A^2 - 6AB =$

16. $15AB^3 + 18BA - 21B^2 =$

Use the distributive property to eliminate the parentheses.

17. $-13(X^2 - 2X + 4) =$

18. $X^2(XY + X^3)$

Solve. Absolute value signs make everything inside of them positive.

Example: $|-3| = 3$ and $|3| = 3$.

19. $\left[15 - 6 + 8^2 \div 2 \div 4\right] \times \left|9^2 - 10^2\right| =$

20. $\left[4 \times 8 - 5 + 2\right]^2 - \left|3 - 6 - 7^2 \times 9\right| =$

Simplify.

1. $x^0 =$

2. $2^{-4} =$

3. $5^{-2} \cdot 5^{-6} =$

4. $9^9 \div 9^3 =$

5. $\left(8^7\right)^5 =$

6. $\left(9^2\right)^0 =$

7. $3^2 M^{-2} N^4 M^{-3} M^{-2} N =$

8. $\dfrac{R^{-6} R P^{-4}}{P^9 R^{-4}} =$

9. $(-1\ 1/5)^2 =$

10. $-2^3 =$

Multiply all the elements of the equation by the least common multiple to simplify, and then solve. Use fractions rather than decimals in your answers.

11. $\dfrac{3}{4} - \dfrac{5}{6} R = \dfrac{7}{10}$

12. $.5Y + .3 = .002$

13. $3\dfrac{2}{3} - \dfrac{5}{12} K = 1\dfrac{1}{4}$

14. $1.203H + .9 = -.6$

Find the greatest common factor, and simplify the expression using parentheses.

15. $56X - 49XA - 28X^2$

16. $4X - 16X^3$

Use the distributive property to eliminate the parentheses.

17. $(2X)^3(X - 5 + 3X^2) =$

18. $5X^2Y(3X + 4YX - X^2Y^3) =$

Solve.

19. $\left[(10+3)^2 - 9\right] \div 20 =$

20. $\left[42 \div 6 - 2\right] \times 11 - 13^2 =$

Simplify.

1. $(1/3)^2 =$

2. $(10^2)^{-4} =$

3. $4^A \cdot 4^B =$

4. $11 \div 11^0 =$

5. $\left(3^D\right)^4 =$

6. $\left(5^3\right)^2 =$

7. $\dfrac{B^5 B^2 C^{-5}}{B^{-4} C^{-3}} =$

8. $\dfrac{D^6 C^{-4} D^2}{D^{-4} C^0 C^2} =$

9. $(-2 \ 3/4)^2 =$

10. $(-10)^4 =$

Multiply all the elements of the equation by the least common multiple to simplify, and then solve. Use fractions rather than decimals in your answers.

11. $-5\dfrac{1}{2} Y - \dfrac{2}{9} = \dfrac{5}{18}$

12. $-.7A + .8A = 1.2$

13. $1\dfrac{2}{3} = -2\dfrac{1}{4} + 1\dfrac{3}{5} A$

14. $3X - 1.6 = .34$

Find the greatest common factor, and simplify the expression using parentheses.

15. $9M - 10M^3 + 19M^2 =$

16. $-36M - 72M^2 + 45M^2$

Use the distributive property to eliminate the parentheses.

17. $A^3(XA + 2X^2A - A^2) =$

18. $AB(A^2 - 4AB + 2B) =$

Solve.

19. $-19 - |(7)(-2)| + 6^2 =$

20. $5 \times 3 + 7^2 - 7 + |-8 \div 4| =$

HONORS APPLICATION PAGES

The next page in this book is entitled Honors.

You will find a special challenge lesson after the last systematic review page for each lesson. These lessons are optional, but highly recommended for students who will be taking advanced math or science courses.

In the honors lessons, you will find a variety of problems that do the following:
- Review previously learned material in an unfamiliar context.
- Provide practical application of math skills relating to science or everyday life.
- Challenge the student with more complex word problems.
- Expand concepts taught in the text.
- Familiarize students with problems that are present in standardized testing.
- Prepare for advanced science courses, such as physics.
- Stimulate logical-thinking skills with interesting or unusual math concepts.

HONORS 4-STEP APPROACH

Here are four steps to help the student receive the most benefit from these pages.

Step 1. Read
Step 2. Think
Step 3. Compare
Step 4. Draw

Step 1. Read

Most of the honors lessons teach new topics or expand on the concepts taught in the regular lessons. Read the explanations carefully. Sometimes you will be led step by step to a new concept. When doing word problems, think through what is being described in the problem before trying to work out the math.

Step 2. Think

It has been suggested that one of the major problems with math instruction in the United States is that students do not take enough time to think about a problem before giving up. One of the purposes of the honors pages is to train you in problem-solving skills. Start by deciding what you already know about the concept being studied, and then look for ways to apply what you know in order to solve the problem. Don't be afraid to leave a difficult problem and come back to it later for a fresh look. You will notice that these lessons do not have as many detailed examples as those in the instruction manual. In real life, individuals must often use what they know in new or unexpected ways in order to solve a problem.

Step 3. Compare

Compare your solution to the one in the back of the instruction manual. If you solved the problem differently, see whether you can follow the given solution. There is often more than one way to solve a problem. The solutions may also give you hints that are not on the lesson pages. If you are not able to solve a problem on your own, do not be upset. Much of this material was purposely designed to stretch your math muscles. You will learn a great deal by giving a problem your best try and then studying the solution.

Step 4. Draw

When in doubt, draw! Often a picture will help you see the big picture and recognize which math skills are necessary to solve the problem.

SCHEDULING HONORS PAGES

Students may not need to do all of the lesson practice pages for each lesson. We do recommend a student finish all of the systematic review pages before attempting the honors page.

If a student needs more time to become comfortable with the new concepts in the text before tackling more advanced problems, he may delay an honors page until he is two or three lessons ahead in the course. The student may also spread one honors section over two or three days while continuing to do the regular student pages. This approach allows time to come back to difficult problems for a fresh look.

Another option is to tackle all the honors pages after finishing the book, as a review and as preparation for the next level. This approach works especially well if you are continuing your study through the summer months.

If you have a pre-2010 teacher manual, go online to MathUSee.com/solutions to access the honors solutions.

If you have a pre-2010 teacher manual, go online to MathUSee.com/solutions to access the honors solutions.

These problems use math skills you should already have. They may be applied in unfamiliar ways.

1. Which of the following operations has the same effect as dividing by three-halves and then multiplying by three-fourth?

    A. multiplying by one-half

    B. multiplying by two

    C. dividing by one-half

    D. dividing by four

    E. dividing by three

2. When $(r - s) = 3$, what is the value of $3(r - s) + \dfrac{(r - s)}{18} - (r - s)^2 - 3$?

3. In the square shown, what is the value of X?

    4X

    X +9

4. Write the area of the square in #3 as an algebraic expression and as a number.

5. As an extra challenge, make an equation with your two answers in #4 equal to each other. Solve for X, and see whether it is the same as your answer for #3.

6. Drew spends four hours a week studying math, and Cameron spends five hours a week. What is the ratio of Drew's time to Cameron's time? For every eight hours that Drew spends, how many hours does Cameron spend?

7. Estimate the slope of the line shown on the graph.

8. Nicole was standing in the center of a circle. She turned carefully so that she was facing 35° away from her starting direction. How many more degrees must she turn in order to be facing in the exact opposite direction from where she started?

Here are some more problems involving exponents.

9. The area of a rectangle is given as $X^4Y^2 + X^2Y$. The length of one side of the rectangle is X^2Y. What is the length of the other side of the rectangle?

10. If the value of X is 2 and the value of Y is 3, what is the area of the rectangle in #9?

Remember that unknowns may not have any value that yields a denominator of zero.

Tell whether the equation is correct or incorrect. If it is incorrect, rewrite the right-hand side correctly.

1. $\dfrac{A^2 + 2A + 3}{A^2 + A + 9} = \dfrac{A^2}{A^2 + A + 9} + \dfrac{2A}{A^2 + A + 9} + \dfrac{3}{A^2 + A + 9}$ correct

2. $\dfrac{X}{X} + \dfrac{Y}{X} = \dfrac{X + Y}{X}$ correct

3. $\dfrac{X^2 + 3X + 6}{X^2 + 2X + 7} = \dfrac{X^2}{X^2} + \dfrac{3X}{2X} + \dfrac{6}{7}$ Incorrect

4. $\dfrac{B}{B} + B^0 = 1$

Simplify by factoring.

5. $\dfrac{4X^2 + X}{X}$

6. $\dfrac{Y^2 + 2Y}{Y}$

7. $\dfrac{4X + 4Y}{2}$

8. $\dfrac{12AB + 16A^2}{4A}$

9. $\dfrac{5XY + 20XYZ}{5YZ}$

10. $\dfrac{2X^2Y - XY^2}{XY}$

Find the common denominator and combine.

11. $\dfrac{6}{X+2} + \dfrac{4X}{X+2} =$

12. $\dfrac{3}{4} + \dfrac{3}{X} =$

13. $\dfrac{7}{4X} - \dfrac{3}{4Y} =$

14. $\dfrac{A}{B} - \dfrac{B}{A} =$

15. $\dfrac{3X}{Y-1} + \dfrac{2X}{Y+1} =$

16. $\dfrac{R}{T} + \dfrac{RS}{RT} =$

Tell whether the equation is correct or incorrect. If it is incorrect, rewrite the right-hand side correctly.

1. $\dfrac{3}{X+1} + \dfrac{6}{X-1} = \dfrac{9}{(X+1)(X-1)}$ correct

2. $\dfrac{1}{4} + \dfrac{2}{4} = \dfrac{3}{8}$ incorrect

$\dfrac{1}{4} + \dfrac{2}{4} = \dfrac{3}{4}$

3. $\dfrac{16}{A-B} = \dfrac{20}{A-B} - \dfrac{4}{A-B}$ correct

4. $\dfrac{X+2}{X+2} - 8^0 = 0$ incorrect

$\dfrac{X+2}{X+2} - 8^0 = \dfrac{X+2}{X+2} - 1$

Simplify by factoring.

5. $\dfrac{Y^4 + Y^2}{Y^2} =$ 1

6. $\dfrac{6X + 3A + 3X}{3} = \dfrac{9X + 3A}{3}$

7. $\dfrac{16X^3Y + 8X^2Y}{2XY} = \dfrac{24x^5Y}{2XY}$

8. $\dfrac{A^2B^3C^4 - ABC^2}{AB} = \dfrac{A^2B^3C^2}{AB}$

9. $\dfrac{2R+2}{(R+1)} = \dfrac{2R+2}{R}$

10. $\dfrac{5X^2 - 5A^2}{5A} = 5X^2 - 5A$

Find the common denominator and combine.

11. $\dfrac{8}{X+2} + \dfrac{-1}{X-2} = \dfrac{9}{X+2}$

12. $\dfrac{1}{2} + \dfrac{6}{AB} = \dfrac{AB}{2AB} + \dfrac{12}{2AB} = \dfrac{12+AB}{2AB}$

13. $\dfrac{8}{2A} - \dfrac{3}{2B} =$

$\dfrac{8 \cdot 2B}{4AB} - \dfrac{3 \cdot 2A}{4AB} = \dfrac{5B-A}{4AB}$

14. $\dfrac{XY}{Z} + \dfrac{ZY}{XY} = \dfrac{XY \cdot XY}{XYZ} + \dfrac{Z \cdot YZ}{XYZ}$

15. $\dfrac{X^2}{3} - \dfrac{X}{2} + \dfrac{2}{3} = \dfrac{2X^2}{18}$

16. $\dfrac{X}{Y} + \dfrac{3Y}{X+1} = \dfrac{X^2+1}{YX+1} + \dfrac{3Y^2}{YX+1}$

Remember that unknowns may not have any value that yields a denominator of zero.

Tell whether the equation is correct or incorrect. If it is incorrect, rewrite the right-hand side correctly.

1. $\dfrac{X}{X} - 2^0 = 0$

2. $\dfrac{2X + 3}{X + 6} = \dfrac{2X}{X} + \dfrac{3}{6}$

Simplify the expression.

3. $\dfrac{BX + BC}{B} =$

4. $\dfrac{27Y^2 - 54}{9} =$

5. $\dfrac{8X^2Y^4 + 4XY^3}{2Y^3} =$

Find the common denominator and combine.

6. $\dfrac{A}{B} + \dfrac{C}{2B} =$

7. $\dfrac{X}{4} + \dfrac{Y}{7} =$

8. $\dfrac{5}{X} + \dfrac{X}{5} =$

Simplify.

9. $3X^4 \cdot 2X^5 =$

10. $X^2 X^{-2} =$

11. $\left(10^2\right)^{-4} =$

12. $2^{15} = \left(2^X\right)^5$, $\quad$ X =

13. $\dfrac{X^{-3}Y^{-2}Y^{-1}}{Y^{-3}X^{-5}}$

14. $\dfrac{A^3 A^{-2} B^2}{B^{-2} A^4}$

Multiply all the elements of the equation by the least common multiple to simplify, and then solve.

15. $2\dfrac{1}{2} = \dfrac{2}{5}P - 1\dfrac{3}{7}$

16. $.2X + .03X = .69$

Use the distributive property to eliminate the parentheses.

17. $7\left(-B + 2^2 + 3B\right) =$

18. $XYZ(X + Y + Z) =$

Solve.

19. $-4 \cdot 3^2 + 2 - 5 - |6 - 22| =$

20. $(6 + 3)^2 - (4 - 8)^2 + 3 \div 1/3 =$

2D

Tell whether the equation is correct or incorrect. If it is incorrect, rewrite the right-hand side correctly.

1. $\dfrac{1}{3} + \dfrac{1}{2} = \dfrac{2}{5}$

2. $\dfrac{2X+1}{4X+6} = \dfrac{2X}{4X+6} + \dfrac{1}{4X+6}$

Simplify the expression.

3. $\dfrac{4X^2X - X^2}{X} =$

4. $\dfrac{(X+1)(X-1)}{(X-1)} =$

5. $\dfrac{28 - 14A^2}{7} =$

Find the common denominator and combine.

6. $\dfrac{8}{X+1} + \dfrac{10}{X+2} =$

7. $\dfrac{7}{4Y} - \dfrac{9}{2Y} =$

8. $\dfrac{A}{B} + \dfrac{B}{C} =$

Simplify.

9. $8^{-5} \div 8^2 =$

10. $\left(\dfrac{1}{2}\right)^{-3} =$

11. $\left(7^2\right)^{-4} =$

12. $1{,}000{,}000 = \left(10^2\right)^X$, X =

13. $\dfrac{6A^3B^3A^{-2}B^{-4}}{2A^{-1}B^0} =$

14. $\dfrac{3A^{-2}B^4A^2}{18BAA^3} =$

Multiply all the elements of the equation by the least common multiple to simplify, and then solve.

15. $\dfrac{1}{2} - \dfrac{2}{5} P = \dfrac{3}{7}$

16. $7.2 - 3 = .07X$

Find the greatest common factor and simplify the expression using parentheses.

17. $-72XY^2 + 45X^2Y =$

18. $18A^2 - 24AB^3 =$

Solve.

19. $(1 - 7)^2 - 8N + 11 = -3$

20. $B(6 + 6)^2 + |100 - 1^2| - 14 = 5 \cdot 9 + 4$

Tell whether the equation is correct or incorrect. If it is incorrect, rewrite the right-hand side correctly.

1. $\dfrac{X+3}{X} = 1 + \dfrac{3}{X}$

2. $\dfrac{2}{X+1} + \dfrac{3}{X} = \dfrac{2}{X+1} + \dfrac{3+1}{X+1}$

Simplify the expression, if possible.

3. $\dfrac{AX - 6Y + 6X}{2} =$

4. $\dfrac{B^4 - B^2}{B^2} =$

5. $\dfrac{6A^2 + 6A}{12A} =$

Find the common denominator and combine.

6. $\dfrac{4}{X} + \dfrac{1}{3} =$

7. $\dfrac{X}{Y} + \dfrac{4Y}{X+2} =$

8. $\dfrac{3}{Q+1} + \dfrac{2}{Q} =$

Simplify.

9. $2^2 X^3 \cdot 2^3 X^{-1} =$

10. $\dfrac{Y^3}{Y^3} =$

11. $\left[\left(5^2\right)^4\right]^{-3} =$

12. $\left(49^3\right) = \left(7^2\right)^3 =$

13. $\left(x^2\right)^3\left(x^{-4}\right)^2 =$

14. $\left(p^{-4}\right)^{-2} p^3 p^{-1} =$

Multiply all the elements of the equation by the least common multiple to simplify, and then solve.

15. $.024\,F + F = .56$

16. $10\frac{2}{3}B + 3\frac{1}{6} = 1\frac{7}{8}$

Use the distributive property to eliminate the parentheses, and add like terms when possible.

17. $100(2.3X - .07Y) =$

18. $1000\,(.009A + .02 + 3) =$

Solve.

19. $(6 \div 9) \cdot 2 - 9Y = 8(Y - 4 + 7)$

20. $(11 - 4)^2 \div 7 - |3 - 9| = 14(R - 2R)$

Work problems are interesting and useful applications of rational expressions. Study the example, and then try some for yourself.

Example 1
If a professional gardener can weed your garden in 6 hours, and his helper can weed it in 10 hours, how long will it take them to do the job if they work together?

The formula for this kind of problem is "rate of work x time worked = portion of job completed," or rt = p.

Look at the problem in chart form. t = time worked in hours.

	rate of work	x time worked	= portion of job completed
Professional	1/6	t	t/6
Helper	1/10	t	t/10

Since it takes the professional six hours to weed the garden, he can weed one-sixth of the garden in one hour. The helper can weed one-tenth of the garden in one hour. Working together at those rates, they will complete one whole job. Add the portions each completed and make them equal to one.

$$\frac{t}{6} + \frac{t}{10} = 1$$

Now solve for t to find how many hours are necessary to complete the job.

$$30\left(\frac{t}{6} + \frac{t}{10} = 1\right) \rightarrow 5t + 3t = 30$$
$$8t = 30$$
$$t = 3 \ 3/4 \text{ hours or 3 hours 45 minutes}$$

Always take a minute to think whether your solution is a logical answer to the original question. Making a chart is optional.

1. A man can paint his garage in 8 hours and his son can paint it in 12 hours. How long will it take to paint the garage if father and son are working together?

2. Sally can make the family's dinner salad in 30 minutes. Her younger sister, Sue, can make the dinner salad in 45 minutes. How long would it take if they worked together? (In this case, *t* will represent minutes, not hours.)

3. If our goat is alone, it can eat all the grass and weeds in our field in 20 days. If our cow is alone, it can eat the same field in 10 days, and if our sheep is alone, it can eat the field in 12 days. If all three animals are allowed to graze at the same time, how long will it be until all the grass and weeds are eaten? (Assume that all the animals will eat the same kinds of plants.)

4. Work can also be done by machines or pipes. With both the hot and cold water faucets open and the drain closed, our bathtub can be filled in 15 minutes. If the same tub is full, it can be emptied in 20 minutes with the drain open. If a toddler turns on both faucets and the drain is open, how long will it take for the bathtub to overflow?

Change to scientific notation.

1. 85,000,000

2. .341

3. .00038

4. 9,700,000,000

Multiply using scientific notation.

5. .000073 x .0054 =

6. (58,000,000)(650) =

7. (.098)(.006) =

8. 1,800,000,000 x 2,400,000

Divide using scientific notation.

9. $27,000 \div .009 =$

10. $.0021 \div 340,000 =$

11. $\dfrac{.00042}{.00006} =$

12. $\dfrac{6,800,000,000}{430,000} =$

Simplify, and combine like terms when possible. Write all the variables on one line.

13. $\dfrac{2X^3}{X^3Y^{-2}} - \dfrac{8XY^3}{XY} + \dfrac{7X^3Y^0}{X^4Y^2} =$

14. $\dfrac{AX^3}{X^{-3}} - \dfrac{BX^3}{B^{-1}} + \dfrac{ABX}{X^2B^2} =$

15. $3AB^{-1} + \dfrac{13AB}{A^{-2}B^1} + \dfrac{3}{A^{-1}B} =$

16. $3X^2Y^2X^{-3}Y^0 + 2XY^{-3}6XY =$

LESSON PRACTICE

Change to scientific notation.

1. 360,000,000

2. .0000001

3. .0059

4. 425,000

Multiply using scientific notation.

5. .0063 x 1,200,000 =

6. (16,000)(.007) =

7. (.92)(.0009) =

8. 2,300,000 x 4,000,000,000,000

Divide using scientific notation.

9. $.0024 \div .000003 =$

10. $29,000,000 \div 15,000 =$

11. $\dfrac{9,600,000,000,000}{.02} =$

12. $\dfrac{.00016}{.000008} =$

Simplify, and combine like terms when possible. Make all exponents positive.

13. $\dfrac{R^{12}R^{-3}R^6}{RS^{-3}} + \dfrac{R^3R^{-2}R^0}{R} =$

14. $\dfrac{2X^3Y^3}{X^{-1}Y^{-1}} + \dfrac{8X^5Y^5}{XY} - \dfrac{3^{-1}X^4Y^5}{X^2Y^2} =$

15. $16A^0B^4 + \dfrac{4B^4}{B^2B^5} - 4A =$

16. $2A^6B^{-3}C^3A^{-2} + C^1C^0C^2A^4B^{-3} =$

Change to scientific notation.

1. 62,000

2. .75

3. .0048

4. 3,080,000

Multiply using scientific notation.

5. $(62,000)(.75) =$

6. $(3,080,000)(.0048) =$

Divide using scientific notation.

7. $(3,080,000) \div (.75) =$

8. $(62,000) \div (.0048) =$

Simplify and combine like terms. For this and all subsequent lessons, unknowns may not have values that would result in denominators with values of zero.

9. $8XXY - YX^2Y + \dfrac{2XY}{X^{-1}} =$

10. $4X^2X^{-1} + \dfrac{12X^2}{X^{-3}} + \dfrac{8XX^3}{\left(X^2\right)^2} =$

11. $4A + \dfrac{9AB^2B^{-1}}{B^1} + 8AB =$

12. $2ABA^{-1} + 3AB - 5B =$

Simplify.

13. $\dfrac{75A^2Y - 50AX}{5AX}$

14. $\dfrac{12XY + 30Y}{3Y}$

Find the common denominator and combine.

15. $\dfrac{Y}{X+1} + \dfrac{3}{2Y} =$

16. $\dfrac{3}{7} + \dfrac{A}{B} =$

Simplify.

17. $\left(10^3\right)^4$

18. $\dfrac{X^{-3}X^2Y^4}{Y^{-2}Y^{-1}X^{-1}}$

Distribute.

19. $XY(3X - 4Y) =$

20. $\dfrac{Y^2}{X}\left(\dfrac{X^3}{Y} + \dfrac{Y^2}{Y}\right) =$

Change to scientific notation.

1. 25,000,000

2. .000039

3. .000000014

4. 760

Multiply using scientific notation.

5. (.000000014)(.000039) =

6. (25,000,000)(760) =

Divide using scientific notation.

7. (.000000014) ÷ (.000039) =

8. (25,000,000) ÷ (760) =

Simplify and combine like terms when possible.

9. $\dfrac{X^3Y^2X^{-1}}{Y} - \dfrac{4Y^2X^2Y^{-2}}{Y} - \dfrac{3X^2Y}{X^2X}$

10. $\dfrac{30X^2Y^{-1}}{Y^1X^3} - \dfrac{11X^1Y^{-1}}{Y^3X^2} - \dfrac{18^0X^0X^{-1}}{Y^4X^2Y^{-2}}$

11. $\dfrac{13A}{B^0} - \dfrac{2A^3B^1}{BAA} - \dfrac{4B^2B^{-2}}{24B^2}$

12. $3ABB^3B^{-2} - 17BA^{-1}A^2 - 42B^{-2}A$

Simplify.

13. $\dfrac{48B^2Y + 72B^2Y}{24B^2} =$

14. $\dfrac{21X^2 - 35XY}{14X} =$

Find the common denominator and combine.

15. $\dfrac{2X}{Y+1} + \dfrac{7}{X-2} =$

16. $\dfrac{A}{7} + \dfrac{7}{A^2}$

Simplify.

17. $-\left(2^{-3}\right)^2$

18. $\dfrac{A^{-6}B^3A^{-2}A^7}{B^{-2}B^{-1}}$

Distribute.

19. $2A^{-2}B^5\left(3AB - 5B^{-3}\right) =$

20. $\dfrac{X}{Y^{-2}}\left(\dfrac{X^2Y}{X} + \dfrac{Y}{X^3}\right) =$

Change to scientific notation.

1. 9,400

2. .00000053

3. .012

4. 160,000

Multiply using scientific notation.

5. $(9,400)(.012) =$

6. $(160,000)(.00000053) =$

Divide using scientific notation.

7. $(9,400) \div (.012) =$

8. $(160,000) \div (.00000053) =$

Simplify and combine like terms.

9. $\dfrac{25X^{-1}Y^2}{YX} - \dfrac{11Y^0X^0}{XXY^{-1}} - \dfrac{2X}{XY^{-2}}$

10. $\dfrac{13X^2Y}{XY^2} - \dfrac{7X^2Y}{Y^{-1}X^{-1}} + \dfrac{5X^0Y^{-1}X}{Y^3}$

11. $\dfrac{3A^2}{B} - \dfrac{2^1 2BB}{A^{-2}A} - 4A^{-2}B$

12. $4ABA^{-1}B + 3AB^{-2}B^3 - 5B^3A^{-1}B^{-1}A$

Simplify.

13. $\dfrac{6X^2 + 4X^3}{12X}$

14. $\dfrac{32X^2 + 4X + 16}{8X}$

Find the common denominator and combine.

15. $\dfrac{4A}{A+5} + \dfrac{6}{A} =$

16. $\dfrac{X}{X^2Y} + \dfrac{2Y}{XY} =$

Simplify.

17. $\left(-4^2\right)^{-1}$

18. $\dfrac{3^3 A^{-3} B^1 C^{-2}}{3^{-1} C^2 A^{-4} B^3}$

Distribute.

19. $5^2 A^2 B^{-3}\left(A^{-4} + AB^2\right) =$

20. $\dfrac{X}{Y}\left(\dfrac{X^3}{Y^{-1}} + \dfrac{Y^3 X}{X^3}\right) =$

Here is another work problem for you.

1. The professional gardener in the example on 2H can weed your garden in six hours, and his helper can weed it in ten hours. The gardener decided to work for two hours by himself, and then have his helper finish the job alone. How long did it take the helper to finish the job?

The rates of work are the same as on 2H. This time, we are told how long the professional worked. Fill in the chart, and then set up and solve the equation.

	rate of work	x time worked	= portion of job completed
Professional	1/6		
Helper	1/10		

Scientific notation is often used when working with very large or very small measurements. An important concept to remember is the fact that measurements are always approximate. Therefore, it is important to use the correct number of ***significant digits*** in your answer. Review the following information. (There is a lesson on this in *Algebra 1*.)

All digits except zero are always counted as significant digits. The number 25 has two significant digits, 31.4 has three significant digits, and .456 also has three significant digits.

Zero may or may not be a significant digit, depending on its position. The number 6,007 has four significant digits because it represents a measure that is accurate to the nearest unit. The number 6,700 has only two significant digits and two place holders, because it may have been rounded to the nearest hundred.

The number .006 has one significant digit and two zeros that are merely place holders. However 6.0 and .60 both have two significant digits because the zeros have been added to show that the measurement is accurate to a certain place value.

The next page has problems to practice this skill.

Tell how many significant digits are in each of the following measurements.

2.   13,456 ft

3.   2,000 m

4.   1,608 in

5.   .59 cm

6.   .068 km

7.   1.3 mi

8.   .400 m

9.   3.000 ft

There are special terms used to name the parts of a number written in scientific notation. The first part of the expression is the *mantissa* and the exponent is the *characteristic*. An example is 2.45×10^{3}. The mantissa is 2.45, and the characteristic is 3. Look at the mantissa of a number written in scientific notation to determine how many significant digits that number has.

Write each measurement in scientific notion and tell how many significant digits it has. The next honors page will tell you how to use significant digits in computations.

10.   245,000,000 ft

11.   .00009 m

12.   1,304 tons

13.   1.50 g

Add or subtract the radicals.

1. $3\sqrt{2} + 6\sqrt{2} =$

2. $5\sqrt{7} - 2\sqrt{5} =$

3. $6\sqrt{X} - 8\sqrt{X} =$

4. $4\sqrt{3} + 16\sqrt{3} =$

Multiply or divide the radicals.

5. $\left(2\sqrt{5}\right)\left(3\sqrt{6}\right) =$

6. $\dfrac{10\sqrt{5}}{2\sqrt{5}} =$

7. $\left(9\sqrt{X}\right)\left(2\sqrt{Y}\right) =$

8. $\dfrac{16\sqrt{20}}{8\sqrt{10}} =$

Simplify.

9. $\dfrac{5}{\sqrt{2}} =$

10. $\dfrac{4\sqrt{6}}{\sqrt{3}} =$

11. $\dfrac{\sqrt{12}}{\sqrt{6}} =$

12. $\dfrac{9\sqrt{27}}{\sqrt{2}} =$

Simplify, and then add or subtract.

13. $\dfrac{2}{\sqrt{5}} + \dfrac{4}{\sqrt{6}} =$

14. $-\sqrt{2}\left(3\sqrt{12} + 2\sqrt{18}\right) =$

15. $\dfrac{X}{\sqrt{2}} + \dfrac{X}{\sqrt{7}} =$

16. $4\left(2\sqrt{10} - \sqrt{20}\right) =$

Add or subtract the radicals.

1. $7\sqrt{A} - 5\sqrt{A} =$

2. $2\sqrt{10} + 4\sqrt{10} =$

3. $6\sqrt{3} + 6\sqrt{5} =$

4. $3\sqrt{11} - 5\sqrt{11} =$

Multiply or divide the radicals.

5. $\left(3\sqrt{6}\right)\left(3\sqrt{5}\right) =$

6. $\dfrac{24\sqrt{14}}{6\sqrt{2}} =$

7. $\left(7\sqrt{A}\right)\left(2\sqrt{A}\right) =$

8. $\dfrac{14\sqrt{X}}{7\sqrt{X}} =$

Simplify.

9. $\dfrac{X}{\sqrt{Y}} =$

10. $\dfrac{3\sqrt{7}}{\sqrt{2}} =$

11. $\dfrac{2\sqrt{3}}{\sqrt{6}} =$

12. $\dfrac{5\sqrt{5}}{\sqrt{10}} =$

Simplify, and then add or subtract.

13. $\dfrac{6}{\sqrt{2}} + \dfrac{10}{\sqrt{7}} =$

14. $\sqrt{6}\left(2\sqrt{7} + 8\sqrt{5}\right) =$

15. $\dfrac{-B}{\sqrt{A}} + \dfrac{-A}{\sqrt{B}} =$

16. $11\left(3\sqrt{24} + 2\sqrt{60}\right) =$

Simplify.

1. $3\sqrt{169A^4}$

2. $3\sqrt{X} + 4\sqrt{X}$

3. $\left(3\sqrt{2}\right)\left(4\sqrt{8}\right) =$

4. $\sqrt{2}\left(6\sqrt{2} + 5\sqrt{8}\right) =$

5. $\dfrac{5\sqrt{30}}{\sqrt{6}} =$

6. $\dfrac{\sqrt{56}}{\sqrt{8}} =$

7. $2\sqrt{27} =$

8. $4\sqrt{75} =$

9. $\dfrac{5}{\sqrt{3}} =$

10. $\dfrac{3}{\sqrt{5}} + \dfrac{4}{\sqrt{6}} =$

Solve using scientific notation.

11. $(6,100)(.000045) =$

12. $(.0000098)(140) =$

13. $(630,000) \div (9,000,000,000) =$

14. $\dfrac{(.000093)(.00000006)}{(300)} =$

Combine like terms.

15. $\dfrac{3A^{-2}B^{-4}C^{-2}}{AB^{-2}} + \dfrac{6ABC^{-3}}{C^{-1}B^{-1}} - \dfrac{4AB^4C}{C^3B^2} =$

Solve.

16. $\dfrac{2X}{5} - \dfrac{3X}{10} = 25$

Simplify.

17. $\left(-2X^2Y\right)\left(3XY^5\right) =$

18. $36X^5Y^2Z^{-2} \div 9X^0Y^4Z^{-3} =$

Solve for X.

19. $\dfrac{5X}{3} = 30$

20. $.3X + 20 = 10 + .5X$

4D

Simplify.

1. $4\sqrt{\dfrac{25}{64}X^2} =$

2. $2\sqrt{10} - 3\sqrt{5} =$

3. $\left(8\sqrt{11}\right)\left(2\sqrt{11}\right) =$

4. $\sqrt{3}\left(8\sqrt{10} - 9\sqrt{5}\right) =$

5. $\dfrac{4\sqrt{48}}{\sqrt{8}} =$

6. $\dfrac{\sqrt{84}}{\sqrt{2}} =$

7. $5\sqrt{80} =$

8. $6\sqrt{125} =$

9. $\dfrac{7}{\sqrt{2}} =$

10. $\dfrac{9}{\sqrt{3}} + \dfrac{6}{\sqrt{2}} =$

Solve using scientific notation.

11. $(58)(.000000037) =$

12. $(.0000000046)(82,000,000) =$

13. $(.0000096) \div (32) =$

14. $\dfrac{(.0000012)(18)}{(.00000054)} =$

Combine like terms.

15. $\dfrac{9X^2YZ}{YX} + \dfrac{2XY^{-1}Z^2}{Z^3Y^{-2}} - \dfrac{6X^{-2}YZ^3}{X^{-3}Z^4} =$

Solve.

16. $\dfrac{1}{8X} - \dfrac{1}{7X} = 2$

Simplify.

17. $\left(4X^3Y\right)\left(3X^{-4}\right)\left(2X^2\right) =$

18. $48D^{-7}E^5F^4 \div 16E^{-6}F^3 =$

Solve for X.

19. $X + 6 = \dfrac{4X}{7}$

20. $\dfrac{3X+2}{4} - 5 = \dfrac{X+8}{2} - 8$

Simplify.

1. $X\sqrt{49X^2Y^2} =$

2. $4\sqrt{6} + 1\sqrt{6} =$

3. $\left(5\sqrt{X}\right)\left(6\sqrt{Y}\right) =$

4. $\sqrt{6}\left(\sqrt{7} + 4\sqrt{6}\right) =$

5. $\dfrac{10\sqrt{63}}{\sqrt{7}} =$

6. $\dfrac{\sqrt{128}}{\sqrt{8}} =$

7. $\sqrt{200} =$

8. $\dfrac{1}{3}\sqrt{72} =$

9. $\dfrac{8}{\sqrt{10}} =$

10. $\dfrac{10}{\sqrt{7}} + \dfrac{16}{\sqrt{11}} =$

Solve using scientific notation.

11. $(.00034)(.00000026) =$

12. $(77,000)(740,000,000) =$

13. $(490,000) \div (.007) =$

14. $\dfrac{(28,000,000)(210,000,000)}{(.98)} =$

Simplify, and combine like terms when possible.

15. $\dfrac{2Q^{-1}R^0T^2}{T^3R^{-1}Q^2} - \dfrac{5Q^2R^{-3}T^4}{T^1R^{-2}Q^3} + \dfrac{Q^5R^3T^4}{RRQ^2} =$

Solve.

16. $\dfrac{X}{3} - \dfrac{X}{5} = \dfrac{2}{15}$

Simplify.

17. $\left(7AX^3Y^2\right)\left(-X^2Y^{-2}\right) =$

18. $135A^2B^5C^{-3} \div 15A^{-2}B^{-3} =$

Solve for X.

19. $\dfrac{3X}{8} = 11 - 2$

20. $30 - .15X = .6X - 15$

Fill in the chart, write an equation and solve. Be careful when recording the helper's time.

1. A brick mason requires 12 hours to lay a garden wall by himself. After the mason and his helper worked for 3 hours, the mason left to finish a different job. The helper took 12 more hours to finish the job. How long would it have taken for the helper working alone to do the whole job?

	rate of work	x time worked	= portion of job completed
Mason			
Helper			

Here is how to use significant digits when doing computations with measurements. These rules apply only to numbers that are measures, not numbers that represent exact amounts. If 4.5 kilograms of books are packed in each of three boxes, the number three is an exact number and is not considered when finding significant digits. The total weight of the books is given as 13.5 kg.

When adding and subtracting measures, it is obvious that your answer cannot be more precise than the least precise measure you are using. If you add 53 miles and 4.55 miles, you will get 57.55 miles. But since one of the addends is rounded to units, your answer cannot be accurate to the hundredths place. Your answer must be rounded to units as well. In this case, 57.55 is rounded to 58.

Add or subtract, and round your answers to match the least precise measurement in each problem.

2. 250 ft + 12.5 ft =

3. .5 in − .361 in =

4. (5.8×10^4) m $+ (1.2 \times 10^{-2})$ m $=$

5. (6.5×10^5) g $- (3.4 \times 10^3)$ g $=$

When multiplying or dividing measures, your answer must have the same number of significant digits as the measure with the fewest number of significant digits.

Example 2

Two sides of a rectangle are given as 40 cm and 5.10 cm. Multiplying to find the area gives us 204.00. However, because 40 has only one significant digit, we must round our answer to one significant digit as well. Therefore the answer is 200 square cm.

Multiply or divide, and give each answer with the correct number of significant digits.

6. 151 ft x 6 ft $=$

7. .0025 in^2 $\div$ .10 in $=$

8. (2.8×10^2) m x (1.04×10^2) m $=$

9. (3.6×10^8) km^2 $\div$ (1.2×10^4) km $=$

10. The length of a rectangle is given as 19.1 meters and the width as 6 meters. Give the perimeter and area of the rectangle with the correct numbers of significant digits.

There are four practice pages for lesson 5. Two are on factoring and two are on rational expressions.

Find the factors.

1. $X^2 + 7X + 12$

2. $X^2 + 3X + 2$

3. $X^2 + X - 6$

4. $X^2 - 11X + 30$

Use the difference of two squares to find the factors.

5. $X^2 - Y^2$

6. $A^2 - 81$

Factor. These all have coefficients.

7. $2X^2 + X - 3$

8. $3X^2 + 17X + 10$

9. $5X^2 + 14X - 3.$

10. $4X^2 + 21X + 5$

Find the greatest common factor before factoring.

11. $2X^2 + 12X + 16$

12. $X^3 + 6X^2 + 9X$

Use repeated factoring to solve.

13. $A^4 - 81$

14. $X^4 - 17X^2 + 16$

Use factoring to solve, and then check your answers.

15. $3X^2 + 10X + 12 = 4$

16. $X^2 - 49 = 0$

17. $2X^4 = 72X^2$

18. $X^4 - 26X^2 + 27 = 2$

Find the factors.

1. $X^2 + X - 12$

2. $X^2 - 10X + 24$

3. $X^2 - 8X - 9$

4. $X^2 + 7X + 10$

Use the difference of two squares to find the factors.

5. $25A^2 - 25B^2$

6. $4X^2 - 64$

Factor. These all have coefficients.

7. $3A^2 + 4AB + B^2$

8. $6X^2 - 2X - 4$

9. $2X^2 + X - 15$

10. $3X^2 + 20X - 32$

Find the greatest common factor before factoring.

11. $2X^3 + 12X^2 + 16X$

12. $3A^2 - 21A + 18$

Use repeated factoring to solve.

13. $X^8 - 1$

14. $X^4 - 109X^2 + 900$

Use factoring to solve, and then check your answers.

15. $6X^3 + 10X^2 = -4X$

16. $2X^2 - 8X - 14 = 10$

17. $X^3 - 50X = 50X$

18. $-8 = A^2 - 16A + 20$

Combine.

1. $\dfrac{2}{X-1} + \dfrac{6}{X+2} + \dfrac{3}{X^2+X-2} =$

2. $\dfrac{X+2}{X-2} - \dfrac{X+2}{X+2} =$

3. $\dfrac{3}{A} + \dfrac{5}{A+1} =$

4. $\dfrac{3X}{X+3} - \dfrac{2X}{X+2} =$

5. $\dfrac{7}{X+2} + \dfrac{4}{3-X} - \dfrac{2X+1}{X^2-X-6} =$

6. $\dfrac{2X}{X^2-4} + \dfrac{8X}{X+2} - \dfrac{4}{X-2} =$

Simplify.

7. $\dfrac{\dfrac{2}{X}}{\dfrac{X+3}{4X}} =$

8. $\dfrac{2+\dfrac{1}{2}}{6-\dfrac{2}{3}} =$

9. $\dfrac{2-\dfrac{3}{A}}{4+\dfrac{1}{A-1}} =$

10. $\dfrac{\dfrac{X^2+7X+12}{X^2+X-12}}{\dfrac{X^2+3X+2}{X^2-9}} =$

11. $\dfrac{X-\dfrac{5}{Y}}{X+\dfrac{4}{Y}} =$

12. $\dfrac{\dfrac{X^2+X-6}{X^2-11X+30}}{\dfrac{X^2-7X+10}{X^2-10X+24}} =$

Combine.

1. $\dfrac{10}{X+4} + \dfrac{3}{X-4} - \dfrac{2}{X^2-16} =$

2. $\dfrac{A+B}{A-B} + \dfrac{2A}{B} =$

3. $\dfrac{15}{X} + \dfrac{20}{X-1} =$

4. $\dfrac{4X}{X+1} - \dfrac{3Y}{X+1} =$

5. $\dfrac{4}{B-4} + \dfrac{5}{B-5} + \dfrac{B-5}{B^2-9B+20} =$

6. $\dfrac{2X+3}{4X^2+6X} + \dfrac{2X}{2X+3} + \dfrac{3}{2X} =$

Simplify.

7. $\dfrac{\dfrac{A}{B}}{\dfrac{A+B}{AB}} =$

8. $\dfrac{3 - \dfrac{1}{3}}{5 + \dfrac{3}{5}} =$

9. $\dfrac{4 + \dfrac{1}{X}}{5 + \dfrac{X}{X+1}} =$

10. $\dfrac{\dfrac{X^2 + 4X - 5}{X^2 - 3X - 18}}{\dfrac{X^2 + 6X + 5}{X^2 - 8X + 12}} =$

11. $\dfrac{Y - \dfrac{2}{3}}{Y - \dfrac{1}{4}} =$

12. $\dfrac{\dfrac{X^4 - 16}{X^2 - 5X + 4}}{\dfrac{X^2 - 4}{X^2 + 3X - 28}} =$

Find the factors.

1. $X^2 + 9X + 20$

2. $X^2 - 9X + 20$

3. $X^2 - 36$

4. $4X^2 + 8X + 3$

5. $6X^2 + X - 2$

6. $X^2 - X - 20$

7. $20X^4 + 10X^3 - 30X^2$

8. $X^4 - 16$

Solve by factoring to find the roots, and then check your answers in the original equation.

9. $X^2 - 2X = -X + 6$

10. $7 = 4X + X^2 - 5$

Combine.

11. $\dfrac{5}{X} - \dfrac{4}{X-1} =$

12. $\dfrac{3}{X+2} - \dfrac{6}{X-3} + \dfrac{4X}{X^2 - X - 6} =$

13. $\dfrac{1 + \dfrac{1}{3}}{1 - \dfrac{1}{3}} =$

14. $\dfrac{\dfrac{4}{3X}}{\dfrac{X-5}{X}} =$

Simplify.

15. $\dfrac{3\sqrt{32}}{\sqrt{2}} =$

16. $6\sqrt{300} =$

17. $\dfrac{7}{\sqrt{5}} =$

18. $\dfrac{2}{\sqrt{7}} + \dfrac{8}{\sqrt{11}} =$

Solve using scientific notation.

19. $\dfrac{(51{,}000)(600)}{(1{,}700)(.012)} =$

Reduce.

20. $\dfrac{X+4}{X^2 + 6X + 8} =$

$X \neq -2, -4$

Find the factors.

1. $X^2 + 3X - 4$

2. $X^2 - 2X - 15$

3. $X^2 + 7X + 10$

4. $X^2 + 17X + 70$

5. $X^2 - 13X + 42$

6. $5X^2 + X - 4$

7. $3X^2 + 13X - 10$

8. $9X^2 - 1$

Solve by factoring to find the roots, and then check your answers in the original equation.

9. $X^2 + 13X + 20 = -22$

10. $X^2 + X + 7 = 16 + X$

Combine.

11. $\dfrac{2X}{Y} - \dfrac{3}{X} + \dfrac{4}{Y} =$

12. $\dfrac{5}{X-4} - \dfrac{9}{X} + \dfrac{8X}{X^2 - 4X} =$

13. $\dfrac{2 + \dfrac{1}{2}}{5 - \dfrac{1}{8}} =$

14. $\dfrac{X - \dfrac{1}{7}}{\dfrac{1}{7} - X} =$

Simplify.

15. $\dfrac{\sqrt{12}}{3\sqrt{2}} =$

16. $\dfrac{1}{5\sqrt{6}} =$

17. $7\sqrt{80} =$

18. $\dfrac{5}{\sqrt{10}} + \dfrac{4}{\sqrt{13}} =$

Solve using scientific notation.

19. $\dfrac{(140,000)(27,000)}{(420)} =$

Reduce.

20. $\dfrac{X^2 - 9}{X^2 + 6X + 9} =$

$X \neq -3$

Find the factors.

1. $x^2 + 2x - 24$

2. $x^2 + 10x + 9$

3. $x^2 - 7x + 10$

4. $64 - x^2$

5. $2x^2 - 17x + 30$

6. $3x^2 + 8x - 3$

7. $4x^2 - 19x + 12$

8. $x^2 - x - 6$

Solve by factoring to find the roots, and then check your answers in the original equation.

9. $2x^2 - 20x = -36 - 2x$

10. $9x^2 - 20x = -16 + 4x$

Combine.

11. $\dfrac{X-3}{2X} - \dfrac{X-2}{2Y} =$

12. $\dfrac{8X-2}{X^2+5X+6} - \dfrac{X+2}{X+3} =$

13. $\dfrac{4+\dfrac{1}{4}}{6-1\dfrac{2}{3}} =$

14. $\dfrac{\dfrac{5X}{2}+1}{2X-\dfrac{4}{3X}} =$

Simplify.

15. $\dfrac{20\sqrt{15}}{5\sqrt{3}} =$

16. $\dfrac{2}{\sqrt{10}} =$

17. $9\sqrt{40} =$

18. $\dfrac{6}{\sqrt{7}} + \dfrac{9}{\sqrt{5}} =$

Solve using scientific notation.

19. $\dfrac{(26,000)(.00004)}{(1,300,000)(200,000,000)} =$

Reduce.

20. $\dfrac{X^2+7X+10}{X^2+4X+4} =$

$X \neq -2$

In math, we are often interested in the relationship between two variables. One of the variables may be *dependent* on the other. When doing equations, watch to see how changing one variable changes others in the same equation.

Read and answer the questions.

1. The distance that a car will travel at a given rate of speed is dependent on the time it travels.

   "Distance = rate x time" or d = rt.
   Given: t = 3 hr and r = 40 mph   What is the distance traveled?

2. Keep the rate the same as in #1 and double the time to six hours. What is the new distance? By what factor has the distance been increased?

3. Given: t = 5 hr and r = 60 mph. What is the distance traveled? Keep the rate the same and double the time to 10 hours. What is the new distance? By what factor has the distance been increased?

4. Given the equation X = RQ, what do you predict will happen to the value of X if the value of Q is doubled?

5. The area of a square is dependent on the length of one side. This may be written as $A = S^2$. If S is 5, what is the area of the square?

6. If the length of each side of the square in #5 is doubled to 10, what is the new value of S^2? By what factor has the area of the square been increased?

7. Find the area of a square with S = 4. Now double the length of the side to 8 and find the new area. By what factor has the area of the square been increased?

8. Given the equation $X = Y^2$, what do you predict will happen to the value of X if the value of Y is doubled?

9. If the area and width of a rectangle are known, the length may be found by dividing. The formula is $L = A \div W$. If the area is 12 and the width is 2, what is the length of the rectangle?

10. Double the width given in #9. If the area is the same, what is the new length? Did the length of the rectangle increase or decrease with the change in width? What is the factor of the increase or decrease?

11. Given the equation $X = R \div T$, what do you predict will happen to the value of X if the value of T is doubled? You may wish to try another example using numbers.

Simplify.

1. $\left(16^{1/2}\right)^3$

2. $\left(x^{3/4}\right)^{8/3}$

3. $\left(2^6\right)^{1/3}$

4. $\left[(-4)^2\right]^{3/4}$

5. $\left(3^{-4}\right)^{1/2}$

6. $\left[\left(\dfrac{4}{9}\right)^{1/2}\right]^3$

7. $\left(\dfrac{1}{2}\right)^{-3}$

8. $\left(x^{AB}\right)^{1/A}$

9. $\left[(-6)^2\right]^{1/2}$

10. $\left(27^{2/3}\right)^2$

Rewrite using fractional exponents, and then simplify.

11. $\sqrt{\sqrt{X}}$

12. $\left(\sqrt[3]{125}\right)^2$

13. $\sqrt[3]{B^5}$

14. $\sqrt{\sqrt[3]{64}}$

15. $\left(\sqrt{36}\right)^3$

16. $\sqrt{\sqrt{25}}$

17. $\left(\sqrt[6]{64}\right)^{-3}$

18. $\sqrt{\sqrt[4]{81}}$

19. $\sqrt{\sqrt{A^{16}}}$

20. $\left(\sqrt[3]{8}\right)^5$

Simplify.

1. $\left(32^{2/5}\right)^2$

2. $\left(2^{2/3}\right)^{1/4}$

3. $\left(x^3\right)^{1/4}$

4. $\left[(-3)^3\right]^{2/9}$

5. $\left(2^{-3}\right)^{1/3}$

6. $\left[\left(\dfrac{16}{81}\right)^{1/8}\right]^2$

7. $\left(\dfrac{1}{3}\right)^{-4}$

8. $\left(B^{Y/X}\right)^{2X/Y}$

9. $\left[(5)^2\right]^{-1/2}$

10. $\left(9^{1/4}\right)^2$

Rewrite using fractional exponents, and then simplify.

11. $\sqrt{\sqrt{x^4}}$

12. $\left(\sqrt[3]{64}\right)^4$

13. $\sqrt[3]{8^5}$

14. $\sqrt{\sqrt[4]{16}}$

15. $\left(\sqrt{49}\right)^2$

16. $\sqrt[4]{A^8}$

17. $\left(\sqrt[3]{216}\right)^{-2}$

18. $\sqrt{\sqrt{100}}$

19. $\sqrt{\sqrt{81}}$

20. $\left(\sqrt[5]{32}\right)^4$

Simplify.

1. $\left(16^{1/4}\right)^3$

2. $\left(5^6\right)^{1/3}$

3. $\left(x^{2/3}\right)^3$

4. $\left(100^{1/2}\right)^5$

Rewrite using fractional exponents, and then simplify.

5. $\sqrt[3]{\sqrt{x}}$

6. $\left(\sqrt[3]{27}\right)^2$

7. $\sqrt{\sqrt[4]{16}}$

8. $\left(\sqrt{25}\right)^4$

Find the factors.

9. $x^2 - 5x - 14$

10. $25x^2 - 1$

11. $2x^2 - 5x - 3$

12. $\dfrac{1}{9}x^2 - \dfrac{36}{25}$

Solve by factoring to find the roots, and then check your answers in the original equation.

13. $5X^2 - 20X - 10 = 5X - 40$

14. $X^2 + 25 = -10X$

Combine.

15. $\dfrac{7X}{X+2} - \dfrac{2X}{X+4} =$

16. $\dfrac{3X}{X+5} - \dfrac{5X}{X^2-25} + \dfrac{8}{X-5} =$

Simplify.

17. $\dfrac{4 - \dfrac{1}{X}}{X + \dfrac{1}{2X}} =$

18. $\dfrac{X^3 - X}{2X^2 + 12X + 18} \div \dfrac{X^2 + 2X + 1}{X^3 - 9X} =$

19. $\dfrac{4\sqrt{2}}{\sqrt{5}} =$

20. $\dfrac{7}{\sqrt{8}} - \dfrac{8}{\sqrt{9}} =$

Simplify.

1. $\left(81^{3/4}\right)^2$

2. $\left(27^{2/3}\right)^2$

3. $\left(16^{5/4}\right)^2$

4. $\left(32^{2/5}\right)^3$

Rewrite using fractional exponents, and then simplify.

5. $\sqrt[3]{\sqrt{64}}$

6. $\left(\sqrt[3]{8}\right)^5$

7. $\sqrt{\sqrt[3]{125}}$

8. $\left(\sqrt{100}\right)^4$

Find the factors.

9. $X^2 + 6X + 9$

10. $X^2 - 25$

11. $X^2 - 2X - 99$

12. $4X^2 - 12X + 9$

Solve by factoring to find the roots, and then check your answers in the original equation.

13. $X^2 - 42 + 3X = 2X$

14. $2X + 15 = X^2$

Solve for X.

15. $\dfrac{X + 4}{X - 8} = 7$ $\qquad X \neq 8$

Combine.

16. $\dfrac{X - 2}{X + 3} - \dfrac{X - 4}{X^2 - 9} + \dfrac{X + 4}{X - 3}$

Simplify.

17. $\dfrac{\dfrac{2}{X} + \dfrac{3}{Y}}{\dfrac{2}{XY}} =$

18. $\dfrac{X^2 - 25}{2X^2 - 18} \div \dfrac{5X - 25}{2X^2 - 6X} =$

19. $\dfrac{8}{\sqrt{10}} =$

20. $\dfrac{6}{\sqrt{2}} - \dfrac{3}{\sqrt{6}} =$

Simplify.

1. $\left(49^{1/2}\right)^3$

2. $(125)^{4/3}$

3. $\left(1,000^{5/3}\right)$

4. $\left(-32^{3/5}\right)^2$

Rewrite using fractional exponents, and then simplify.

5. $\sqrt{\sqrt{81}}$

6. $\left(\sqrt{36}\right)^3$

7. $\sqrt{\sqrt[4]{X^8}}$

8. $\left(\sqrt[3]{1000}\right)^{-5}$

Find the factors.

9. $X^2 - 4X + 4$

10. $X^2 + 10X + 25$

11. $X^2 - 12X + 36$

12. $3X^2 + 14X - 5$

Solve by factoring to find the roots, and then check your answers in the original equation.

13. $42 - 3X^2 = 15X$

14. $X^2 - 25 = X - 5$

Combine.

15. $\dfrac{8}{3X} - \dfrac{2}{2X} - \dfrac{5}{6X^2} =$

16. $\dfrac{X-3}{X-2} - \dfrac{4X+3}{X^2-4} - \dfrac{X+3}{X+2} =$

17. $\dfrac{\dfrac{1}{9} - \dfrac{X}{3}}{\dfrac{X}{12} + \dfrac{5}{8}} =$

18. $\dfrac{X^2 - 6X - 16}{X+2} \div \dfrac{X^2 - 8X + 16}{X-4} =$

Simplify.

19. $\dfrac{\sqrt{5}}{\sqrt{3}}$

20. $\dfrac{1}{\sqrt{7}} - \dfrac{2}{\sqrt{8}}$

A *golden rectangle* is a rectangle with a particular relationship between its sides. Many people consider it to have the most pleasing proportions of any rectangle. In *Geometry* 10H, we learned how to construct a golden rectangle geometrically. Now we are going to explore the rectangle using algebra.

Follow the directions to find the value of the golden ratio.

To construct a golden rectangle, start by drawing a square. Next find the midpoint of one side of the square, and draw a diagonal to B. The length of MB becomes the length of MG.

The small rectangle BFGD and the new large rectangle AFGC are proportional (similar), and each is a golden rectangle. Stated as a ratio:

$$\frac{\text{long side (small rectangle)}}{\text{short side (small rectangle)}} = \frac{a}{b} = \frac{a+b}{a} = \frac{\text{long side (large rectangle)}}{\text{short side (large rectangle)}}$$

1. Instead of *a*, we will call the length of one side of the square 2X. What is the length of $\overline{MD}$?

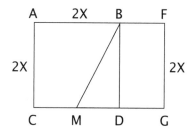

2. Using your answer to #1, find the length of $\overline{MB}$. Keep the radical in your answer. This is also the length of $\overline{MG}$.

3. What is the value of a + b in terms of X? ($\overline{AF}$)

4. What is the value of *b* in terms of X? ($\overline{BF}$ or $\overline{DG}$)

5. Set up a ratio like the one given above #1 for the sides of the large rectangle. This time, state the lengths of the sides in terms of X.

6. Simplify the ratio you wrote in #5, keeping the radical.

7. This **golden ratio** is a value that is often identified with the Greek letter Φ. The long side of a golden rectangle is always Φ (phi) times the short side. Using a calculator, find the actual numerical value of Φ. (This is an irrational value, like π). Record your answer to three decimal places.

8. Measure some common rectangles that appear to be golden rectangles. Try a credit card, a television screen, and different-sized sheets of paper. You may want to use a metric ruler for ease of computation. Divide the long side of each rectangle by the short side, and see how close the result is to the golden ratio.

9. Sometimes the ratio $1/\Phi$ (short side over the long side) is called the golden ratio as well. Find the value of $1/\Phi$ to three decimal places. You may see an uppercase letter (Φ) used for the larger value and a lowercase letter (ϕ) for the smaller value.

10. See whether you can find a fraction that is close to the smaller value of ϕ that you found in #9. Since ϕ is irrational, you will not find an exact match. Experimentation should find a fraction that is close in value.

Simplify.

1. $\sqrt{-1}$ i

2. $\sqrt{-49}$

$7 \cdot i$

3. $\sqrt{-64x^6}$

$i8x^3$

4. $\sqrt{\dfrac{-121}{144}}$

$\dfrac{i11}{12}$

5. $\sqrt{-4} + \sqrt{-100}$

$2\overline{6}$

6. $2\sqrt{-9} + \sqrt{36}$

$2\,i3 + 6$

7. $\sqrt{-20x^2}$

$2x\,i\sqrt{5}$

8. $\sqrt{-A} + \sqrt{-B}$

Simplify, and combine like terms when possible. Always factor out the i first when multiplying the square roots of negative numbers.

9. $3\sqrt{-12} + 4\sqrt{-162} =$

$i\sqrt{2^2 \cdot 3}$

$3 \cdot i2 \cdot \sqrt{3}$

$3i$

$6i\sqrt{3} + 36i\sqrt{2}$

10. $13\sqrt{-1} - 2\sqrt{-81}$

11. $2\sqrt{-25} + \sqrt{16} =$

$2i5 + 4$

12. $\sqrt{3x^2} + \sqrt{4i^2} = 3X\ 1$

13. $i \cdot i \cdot i \cdot i =$

$i^4 = 1$

14. $i \cdot i \cdot i \cdot i \cdot i \cdot i^3 =$

$6i^3$

15. $i^5 =$

$i = \sqrt{-1} = i$

16. $(i^3)^3 = i^9$

17. $(15i)(-8i) =$

$\begin{array}{r} 15 \\ 8 \\ \hline 115 \end{array}$ -115

18. $3i\sqrt{-169}$

19. $\sqrt{-6}\sqrt{-6} =$

20. $\left(2\sqrt{225}\right)\left(6\sqrt{-4}\right)$

Simplify.

1. $\sqrt{-225}$

2. $\sqrt{-121}$

3. $\sqrt{-49A^4}$

4. $\sqrt{\dfrac{-100}{25}}$

5. $\sqrt{-64} - \sqrt{-16}$

6. $3\sqrt{36} - 2\sqrt{-4}$

7. $\sqrt{-45X^9}$

8. $\sqrt{-X^2Y^4} + \sqrt{X^2Y^4}$

Simplify, and combine like terms when possible.

9. $6\sqrt{-200} - 5\sqrt{25} =$

10. $4\sqrt{-2} + 2\sqrt{-50} =$

11. $A\sqrt{-9} + A\sqrt{-81} =$

12. $\sqrt{-X^4} + \sqrt{16X^4i^2} =$

13. $2i^2 \cdot 3i^2 =$

14. $i^2 \cdot i^3 \cdot i^5 =$

15. $i^7 =$

16. $\left(i^4\right)^2 =$

17. $(-10i)(-5i) =$

18. $14i\sqrt{-1} =$

19. $\sqrt{-75}\sqrt{-75} =$

20. $\left(6\sqrt{-169}\right)\left(2\sqrt{-81}\right) =$

Simplify.

1. $\sqrt{-81}$

2. $\sqrt{-169}$

3. $\sqrt{-64X^2}$

4. $\sqrt{\dfrac{-16}{25}}$

5. $\sqrt{-4} + \sqrt{-36}$

6. $\sqrt{-9} + \sqrt{100}$

Simplify, and combine like terms when possible.

7. $5\sqrt{-8} + 7\sqrt{-242}$

8. $(18i)(-7i)$

9. $(i \cdot i \cdot i)$

10. $\left(4\sqrt{-196}\right)\left(3\sqrt{49}\right)$

Simplify.

11. $\left(125^{1/3}\right)^2 \left(25^{1/2}\right)^3$

12. $\left(x^4\right)^{1/3}\left(x^2\right)^{2/3}$

Rewrite using fractional exponents, and then simplify.

13. $\left(\sqrt[4]{10,000}\right)^3$

14. $\sqrt[3]{\sqrt{x^4}}$

Solve by factoring to find the roots, and then check your answers in the original equation.

15. $9X - 3 = -2X^2 + 8$

16. $1/4X^2 = 9$

Simplify.

17. $\dfrac{2X^2}{X^2-16} \div \dfrac{X}{4-X} =$

18. $\sqrt{\dfrac{4}{5}} - \sqrt{\dfrac{1}{2}} =$

Solve using scientific notation.

19. $(1,400)(.00021) \div (.49) =$

Simplify.

20. $\dfrac{4^{-1}X^2Y^{-3}}{X^{-1}Y} - \dfrac{3^2YXY^0}{X^2Y^2} + \dfrac{2^2Y^{-2}}{XX^{-2}} =$

ALGEBRA 2

Simplify.

1. $\sqrt{-16}$

2. $\sqrt{144}$

3. $\sqrt{25X^4}$

4. $\sqrt{\dfrac{-16}{25}}$

5. $\sqrt{-9} + \sqrt{-81}$

6. $\sqrt{16} + \sqrt{-36}$

Simplify, and combine like terms when possible.

7. $\sqrt{20} + 2\sqrt{45}$

8. $(9i)(-8i)$

9. $(2i \cdot 2i)$

10. $\left(7\sqrt{-64}\right)\left(2\sqrt{-81}\right)$

Simplify.

11. $(343)^{2/3}\,(8)^{2/3}$

12. $(1{,}000)^{1/3}(10{,}000)^{2/4}$

Rewrite using fractional exponents, and then simplify.

13. $\left(\sqrt{8,100}\right)^{-1}$

14. $\sqrt{\sqrt[5]{32}}$

Solve by factoring to find the roots, and then check your answers in the original equation.

15. $\dfrac{1}{9}X^2 + \dfrac{25}{9} = \dfrac{10}{9}X$

16. $8X^2 - 40X = -50$

Simplify.

17. $\dfrac{X-5}{X^2 - 10X + 25} \div \dfrac{X+6}{X^2 - 3X - 10} =$

18. $\sqrt{\dfrac{2}{3}} - \sqrt{\dfrac{3}{5}} =$

Solve using scientific notation.

19. $(.03)(60,000,000)(400) =$

Simplify.

20. $\dfrac{3X^2A}{X} - \dfrac{7X^{-2}A}{X^{-3}} - 5XA =$

Simplify.

1. $\sqrt{-4}$

2. $\sqrt{-121}$

3. $\sqrt{-x^2}$

4. $\sqrt{\dfrac{-81}{4}}$

5. $\sqrt{-16} + \sqrt{25}$

6. $\sqrt{-81} + \sqrt{-1}$

Simplify, and combine like terms when possible.

7. $5\sqrt{-12} + 7\sqrt{-75}$

8. $(10i)(10i)(2i)$

9. $(i \cdot i \cdot i \cdot 3i)$

10. $\left(6\sqrt{25}\right)\left(5\sqrt{-16}\right)$

Simplify.

11. $\left(x^3\right)^{2/3}\left(x^5\right)^{4/5}$

12. $\left(x^0\right)^2\left(x^{3/3}\right)^{1/3}$

Rewrite using fractional exponents, and then simplify.

13. $\left(\sqrt[3]{8}\right)^{-2}$

14. $\sqrt[3]{\sqrt{64}}$

Solve by factoring to find the roots, and then check your answers in the original equation.

15. $4/25\ X^2 = 1$

16. $9/4\ X^2 - 4 = 0$

Simplify.

17. $\dfrac{2x^2 + 2X - 4}{5X - 5} \div \dfrac{6X^2 - 6X - 36}{3X + 15} =$

18. $\sqrt{\dfrac{4}{7}} - \sqrt{\dfrac{1}{4}} =$

Solve using scientific notation.

19. $(.0000007)(.0018) \div (3{,}000) =$

Simplify.

20. $-\dfrac{4X}{A} - \dfrac{AA^0}{A^2X^{-1}} + \dfrac{5A^{-2}}{X}$

Math involves rules and patterns that do not change, whether you are using numerals, letters, or other symbols. Sometimes using letters alone can help you see the patterns more clearly. Study the examples.

$$Y^X = Y \text{ times itself X times} \qquad Y^{\frac{1}{X}} = \sqrt[X]{Y} \qquad X^{\frac{a}{b}} = \left(\sqrt[b]{X}\right)^a$$

Simplify each expression. Combine terms when possible, and use radical signs to replace fractional exponents.

1. $A^{\frac{x}{y}}$

2. $Q^R =$

3. $\left(X^{\frac{a}{b}}\right)^{\frac{b}{a}}$

4. $\left(Y^{\frac{a}{b}}\right)^{\frac{c}{d}}$

5. $\left(Y^F \cdot Y^G\right)^{\frac{1}{H}} =$

6. $\left(X^F \cdot Y^F\right)^G =$

7. $\left(M^{\frac{x}{z}} \cdot M^{\frac{y}{z}}\right)^{\frac{z}{y}} =$

8. $\left[\left(X^a\right)^b \cdot X^b\right]^{\frac{1}{c}} =$

9. $\left(P^a + P^a\right)^{\frac{a}{b}} =$

10. $\left(X^E \div X^F\right)^H =$

Find the conjugate.

1. A + B

2. 3X – 8

3. $6 + \sqrt{2}$

4. 1 – 5i

Multiply.

5. (2B + 4)(2B – 4)

6. (3 + 2i)(3 – 2i)

7. (2 + 7i)(2 – 7i)

8. $\left(4 + \sqrt{7}\right)\left(4 - \sqrt{7}\right)$

Use the conjugate to simplify the rational expression (put it in standard form).

9. $\dfrac{X}{3+4i}$

10. $\dfrac{11}{2+i}$

11. $\dfrac{4i}{6-3i}$

12. $\dfrac{i^2}{4+5i}$

13. $\dfrac{Z}{Z+\sqrt{5}}$

14. $\dfrac{8}{8-\sqrt{8}}$

15. $\dfrac{7X}{2-2\sqrt{X}}$

16. $\dfrac{3}{8i+i\sqrt{2}}$

Find the conjugate.

1. $X^2 + Y^2$

2. $7X + 4$

3. $-3 - \sqrt{3}$

4. $5 + 3i^2$

Multiply.

5. $(3 + 8X)(3 - 8X)$

6. $\left(6 - 3i^5\right)\left(6 + 3i^5\right)$

7. $(2 + i)(2 - i)$

8. $\left(4 - 5\sqrt{2}\right)\left(4 + 5\sqrt{2}\right)$

Use the conjugate to simplify the rational expression (put it in standard form).

9. $\dfrac{A}{4A + i}$

10. $\dfrac{9}{3 - i}$

11. $\dfrac{7i^2}{5 - 6i}$

12. $\dfrac{3i}{2 + 8i}$

13. $\dfrac{X^2}{X - \sqrt{4X}}$

14. $\dfrac{6 - 2}{4 + \sqrt{-4}}$

15. $\dfrac{3X + \sqrt{2}}{3X - \sqrt{2}}$

16. $\dfrac{5i}{2i + i\sqrt{3}}$

Find the conjugate.

1. $3X - i$

2. $10 + 2\sqrt{7}$

Multiply.

3. $(5 + 4i)(5 - 4i)$

4. $\left(3X + \sqrt{11}\right)\left(3X - \sqrt{11}\right)$

Find the factors.

5. $4X^2 - 3 = 0$

6. Solve for X in #5.

7. $3Y^2 - 1/9 = 0$

8. Solve for Y in #7.

Simplify, and combine like terms when possible.

9. $11\sqrt{-12} + 6\sqrt{-3}$

10. $(7i)\left(\sqrt{-64}\right)$

11. $\sqrt{-144} \div 4i$

12. $i^2 \cdot i^2$

Simplify.

13. $\left(9^{3/2}\right)^{-2}$

14. $\left(\sqrt[4]{x^8}\right)^{1/2}$

Solve by factoring to find the roots, and then check your answers in the original equation.

15. $6X^2 + 3X + 3 = -4X + 1$

16. $9(X^2 + X) = 25 + 9X$

Simplify.

17. $\dfrac{2X^2}{X^2 - 16} \div \dfrac{X}{4 - X} =$

18. $12\sqrt{\dfrac{1}{3}} - 9\sqrt{\dfrac{2}{5}} =$

19. $\dfrac{60X^{-2}YZ^4}{24X^{-1}Z^3Y^{-1}} =$

20. $\dfrac{4 + \dfrac{X}{Y}}{2 - \dfrac{2X}{Y}} =$

Find the conjugate.

1. $4 + 8i$

2. $2 + 3\sqrt{91}$

Multiply.

3. $(12 + 3i)(12 - 3i)$

4. $\left(x + \sqrt{2}\right)\left(x - \sqrt{2}\right)$

Find the factors.

5. $81X^2 - 3 = 0$

6. Solve for X in #5.

7. $7Y^2 - 9 = 0$

8. Solve for Y in #7.

Simplify, and combine like terms when possible.

9. $6\sqrt{-50} - 5\sqrt{-18}$

10. $\left(5i\right)\left(2\sqrt{-49}\right)$

11. $\sqrt{-225} \div 3$

12. $i^3 \cdot i^3$

Simplify.

13. $\left(9^{2/3}\right)^3$

14. $\left(\sqrt{400}\right)^{-1}$

Solve by factoring to find the roots, and then check your answers in the original equation.

15. $7X^2 + 11X = 2X^2 + 3X + 4$

16. $12X^2 - 6X - 15 = X - 3$

Simplify.

17. $\dfrac{6X^2 + 3X}{4X^2 - 1} \div \dfrac{3X + 12}{2X^2 + X - 1} =$

18. $\sqrt{\dfrac{2}{X}} + \sqrt{\dfrac{3}{X}} =$

19. $\dfrac{5X^{-3}Y^2Z^{-1}}{5^{-2}XY^{-2}Z} =$

20. $\dfrac{5 - \dfrac{X - 2}{X}}{X + \dfrac{5}{2X}} =$

Find the conjugate.

1. $3 - 2i$

2. $4 - 5\sqrt{8}$

Multiply.

3. $(A + 14i)(A - 14i)$

4. $\left(2X + \sqrt{3}\right)\left(2X - \sqrt{3}\right)$

Find the factors.

5. $16X^2 - 15 = 0$

6. Solve for X in #5.

7. $5X^2 - 10 = 0$

8. Solve for X in #7.

Simplify, and combine like terms when possible.

9. $11\sqrt{-12} + 6\sqrt{-3}$

10. $(-3i)\left(5\sqrt{-81}\right)$

11. $\sqrt{-196} \div 2i$

12. $i^4 \cdot i^4$

Simplify.

13. $\left(8^2 + 15^2\right)^{3/2}$

14. $\left(\sqrt[3]{64}\right)^{3/2}$

Solve by factoring to find the roots, and then check your answers in the original equation.

15. $\dfrac{4}{3} X^2 = \dfrac{4}{3} X + 5$

16. $8 - 6X = 3X^2 + X + 10$

Simplify.

17. $\dfrac{X^2 + 2X - 24}{X^2 + 8X + 12} \div \dfrac{X^2 - 8X + 16}{X^2 + 4X + 4} =$

18. $\sqrt{\dfrac{1}{2A}} - \sqrt{\dfrac{3}{2}} =$

19. $\dfrac{3^{-1}X^{-4}Y^3X^2}{3^0Y^{-1}Y^2} =$

20. $\dfrac{3X + \dfrac{5X + 8}{3X}}{2 - \dfrac{4}{X^2}} =$

Here is a chart showing the relationships between different kinds of numbers.

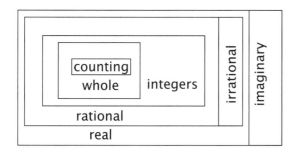

Counting numbers are the ones a child uses to count.

Whole numbers are the counting numbers and zero.

Integers include the negatives of the counting numbers.

Rational numbers can be written as a fraction or ratio.

Irrational numbers are non-repeating, non-terminating decimals.

Give an example of each of the following.

1. A whole number that is not a counting number.

2. An integer that is a not whole number.

3. A rational number that is not an integer.

4. A real number that is not rational.

Mathematicians who study number theory are particularly interested in integers. They have found many fascinating relationships and patterns in our number system. In the middle ages, a man named Leonardo Fibonacci proposed a problem about rabbits that has become famous.

We start at the beginning of month 1 with two rabbits, one male and one female. At the end of two months, the rabbits produce another pair. They continue to produce another pair each month after that. We assume that the pairs of rabbits are always male and female, that a new pair produces another pair each month after they are two months old, and that the rabbits never die.

Fill in the chart and answer the questions.

5. For each month, first sketch the rabbits that already exist. Then decide which of the pairs are old enough to produce a new pair that month, and sketch in the new pairs as well. In the righthand column, put the total number of pairs that are alive that month.

# of months	drawing of pairs	# of pairs
1		1
2		1
3		2
4		
5		

6. Check your answers to #5, and then record the numbers of pairs as a series of numbers: 1, 1, 2 . . . Can you find a pattern in the series?

7. Use the pattern to find the next three numbers in the series (for months 6, 7, and 8).

The numbers in this series are called the **Fibonacci numbers**. They occur in surprising places. For instance, the number of petals on most flowers is a Fibonacci number. Check this for yourself by observing pictures or actual plants.

Expand.

1. $(X + 3)^2$

2. $(A - 3)^2$

3. $(3X + 4)^2$

4. $(2X + 1)^2$

Find the binomial or square roots of the trinomial.

5. $X^2 + 8X + 16$

6. $X^2 - 18X + 81$

7. $A^2 + 16A + 64$

8. $A^2 - 16A + 64$

Expand.

9. $(X + 5)^3$

10. $(3X - 2)^3$

11. $(2A + 2B)^3$

12. $(X - 1)^3$

13. $(Y - 1/4)^3$

14. $(2R + 3)^3$

Write the coefficients of Pascal's triangle for the first five powers.

15.

$$1$$

___ ___

___ ___ ___

___ ___ ___ ___

___ ___ ___ ___ ___

___ ___ ___ ___ ___ ___

Expand.

1. $(A - 4)^2$

2. $(X - Y)^2$

3. $(2X + 5)^2$

4. $(3X - 2)^2$

Find the binomial or square roots of the trinomial.

5. $B^2 + 20B + 100$

6. $X^2 - 2X + 1$

7. $X^2 - 4X + 4$

8. $R^2 + 24R + 144$

Expand.

9. $(X - 10)^3$

10. $(2X + 1)^3$

11. $(A + B)^3$

12. $(X - 5)^3$

13. $(P - 1/3)^3$

14. $(4F + 2)^3$

Write the coefficients of Pascal's triangle for the 6th, 7th, and 8th powers. The 5th power is done for you.

15.

1	5	10	10	5	1

Expand.

1. $(X + 5)^2$

2. $(2X - 3)^2$

Find the binomial roots of the trinomial.

3. $4X^2 + 20X + 25$

4. $X^2 - 14X + 49$

Expand.

5. $(X + 4)^3$

6. $(X - 4)^3$

7. $(2X + 1)^3$

8. $(3X - 2)^3$

9. The conjugate of $13 + 2i\sqrt{5}$ is _____?

10. What are the factors of $9X^2 - 5$?

Simplify so that there are no imaginary numbers or radicals in the denominator.

11. $\dfrac{4\sqrt{6}}{2\sqrt{8}+1}$

12. $\dfrac{7}{4-3i}$

Simplify, and combine like terms when possible.

13. $(8i)(2\sqrt{-2})$

14. $(i^3)^2$

Simplify.

15. $(100^{3/2})^{1/2}$

16. $(\sqrt[3]{x^6})^4$

Solve and check the answer.

17. $6X - 12 = -2X^2 + 4X$

18. $\dfrac{X^2 - 3X - 4}{X^2 + X - 6} \div \dfrac{-6X - 6}{X^2 - 2X} =$

Simplify.

19. $5\sqrt{\dfrac{8}{3}} - 6\sqrt{\dfrac{18}{7}} =$

20. $\dfrac{X^2 - \dfrac{X}{2}}{X + \dfrac{2X}{3}} =$

Expand.

1. $(X + 7)^2$

2. $(3X - 4)^2$

Find the binomial roots of the trinomial.

3. $X^2 - 6X + 9$

4. $4X^2 + 16X + 16$

Expand.

5. $(X + 2)^3$

6. $(X - 1/5)^3$

7. $(3X + 2)^3$

8. $(2X - 3)^3$

9. The conjugate of $5 - \sqrt{-4}$ is _____?

10. What are the factors of $2X^2 - 15$?

Simplify so that there are no imaginary numbers or radicals in the denominator.

11. $\dfrac{10\sqrt{15}}{3\sqrt{5}+8}$

12. $\dfrac{5}{2+6i}$

Simplify, and combine like terms when possible.

13. $(7i)\left(3\sqrt{-8}\right)$

14. i^3

Simplify.

15. $\left(16^{-1/4}\right)^{-3}$

16. $\left(\sqrt{x}\right)^{-3}$

Solve and check the answer.

17. $2x^2 = 5/2x + 3$

18. $\dfrac{6X-42}{X+1} \cdot \dfrac{X^2-1}{-9X+9}$

Simplify.

19. $2\sqrt{\dfrac{3}{5}} - X\sqrt{20} =$

20. $\dfrac{2-\dfrac{3X+4}{5}}{3X+\dfrac{2+X}{3}} =$

Expand.

1. $(X + 8)^2$

2. $(4X + 1)^2$

Find the binomial roots of the trinomial.

3. $X^2 + 8X + 16$

4. $9X^2 + 12X + 4$

Expand.

5. $(X + 6)^3$

6. $(2X + 5)^3$

7. $(X + 4)^3$

8. $(X - 2/3)^3$

9. The conjugate of $6 + 3\sqrt{-9}$ is _____?

10. What are the factors of $100X^2 - 83$?

Simplify so that there are no imaginary numbers or radicals in the denominator.

11. $\dfrac{5\sqrt{7}}{2\sqrt{7}-3}$

12. $\dfrac{4}{10-7i}$

Simplify, and combine like terms when possible.

13. $\left(10i^2\right)\left(\sqrt{-75}\right)$

14. $(2i)^3$

Simplify.

15. $\left(9^{1/2}\right)^{-5}$

16. $\left(\sqrt[3]{x^9}\right)^{-2}$

Solve and check the answer.

17. $5X^2-3X=0$

18. $\dfrac{X^2+5X}{25-X^2}\div\dfrac{X+5}{10X-50}=$

19. $3\sqrt{\dfrac{2}{7}}-7\sqrt{\dfrac{3}{X}}=$

20. $\dfrac{1+\dfrac{4-5X}{2}}{\dfrac{X+3}{4}}$

In your text, you learned how to use Pascal's triangle to find the coefficients of each term that results when a binomial is raised to a power. Pascal's triangle also illustrates other mathematical patterns. This lesson explores some of them.

The *1* at the top of the pyramid is row 0, the two *1*s under it are row 1, and so on.

Follow the directions.

1. Sum the numbers in each row of the triangle, and write the sums below. What pattern can you find in your answers?

Row 0 = ____

Row 1 = ____

Row 2 = ____

Row 3 = ____

Row 4 = ____

Row 5 = ____

Row 6 = ____

```
                      1
                   1     1
                1     2     1
             1     3     3     1
          1     4     6     4     1
       1     5    10    10     5     1
    1     6    15    20    15     6     1
```

2. You are familiar with square numbers like 4, 9, 16, etc. A square number of coins can be arranged to form a square. Triangles can be made using a ***triangular number*** of coins. The first triangular number is 3. Sketch the next three triangular numbers.

3 ⭕ ⭕ ⭕

3. Ignoring the ones, find the triangular numbers on Pascal's triangle and mark them. Without drawing, find the next triangular number.

4. What kind of numbers are produced if you add two adjacent triangular numbers?

5. Carefully draw shallow diagonal lines as shown at right. At the end of each line, write the sum of the numbers it crosses. What special sequence of numbers did you produce?

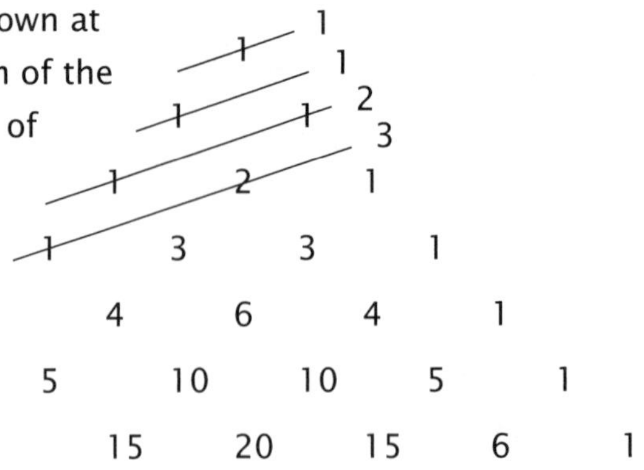

$$
\begin{array}{ccccccc}
 & & & & & 1 & \\
 & & & & 1 & & 1 \\
 & & & 1 & & 2 & \\
 & & & & & 3 & \\
 & & 1 & & 2 & & 1 \\
 & 1 & & 3 & & 3 & 1 \\
1 & & 4 & & 6 & & 4 & & 1 \\
 1 & & 5 & & 10 & & 10 & & 5 & & 1 \\
1 & & 6 & & 15 & & 20 & & 15 & & 6 & & 1
\end{array}
$$

There are other patterns as well in Pascal's triangle. See whether you can find them yourself, or do some research at your library or on the web.

Factorials have several interesting applications. They may look strange but are actually quite easy to understand. A factorial can be written as "a!" and is read "a factorial." Look at the examples.

one factorial = 1! = 1   two factorial = 2! = 2 x 1 = 2

three factorial = 3! = 3 x 2 x 1 = 6

6. Find the value of 4!

7. Find the value of 5!

Factorials can be simplified, as shown in this example.

$$\frac{8!}{5!} = \frac{8 \cdot 7 \cdot 6 \cdot \cancel{5} \cdot \cancel{4} \cdot \cancel{3} \cdot \cancel{2} \cdot \cancel{1}}{\cancel{5} \cdot \cancel{4} \cdot \cancel{3} \cdot \cancel{2} \cdot \cancel{1}} = 336$$

Simplify.

8. $\dfrac{9!}{7!} =$ 9. $\dfrac{6!}{3!\ 3!} =$

10. $\dfrac{201!}{200!} = \dfrac{201 \cdot 200!}{200!} =$

You don't need to write this all out.

For #1–4, tell how many terms there will be and expand.

1. $(A + 7)^6$

2. $(X - 2)^5$

3. $(3X + 1)^4$

4. $(R - 1/2)^6$

5. What is the fourth term of $(A + 2B)^5$?

6. What is the third term of $(X + 2)^6$?

7. What is the fifth term of $(2X - 2)^7$?

8. What is the second term of $(X - 1/3)^4$?

9. What is the fourth term of $(X + Y)^6$?

10. What is the sixth term of $(P - Q)^8$?

For # 1–4, tell how many terms there will be and expand.

1. $(B + 4)^3$

2. $(2X + 1)^6$

3. $(R - T)^5$

4. $(1/2\ X + 1/2\ Y)^4$

5. What is the first term of $(X + 2Y)^{10}$?

6. What is the last term of $(A + B)^6$?

7. What is the third term of $(2X + 3)^4$?

8. What is the fifth term of $(Q + 2/3)^6$?

9. What is the second term of $(3R - T)^5$?

10. What is the fourth term of $(2X - 2Y)^4$?

Answer the questions.

1. How many terms are in $(X + 3)^5$?

2. Expand $(X + 3)^5$.

3. How many terms are in $(X - 4)^6$?

4. Expand $(X - 4)^6$.

5. What is the fourth term of $(2X + Y)^4$?

6. What is the second term of $(2X + Y)^4$?

7. What is the third term of $(X - 2)^6$?

8. What is the fifth term of $(X - 2)^6$?

9. Expand $(X + 3A)^2$.

10. Find the binomial root of the trinomial $9X^2 - 42X + 49$.

11. Expand $(X + 12)^3$.

12. Expand $(2X - 1/3)^3$.

Simplify so that there are no imaginary numbers or radicals in the denominator.

13. $\dfrac{2\sqrt{2} + 1}{3\sqrt{3} - 1}$

14. $\dfrac{-8i}{4 + 5i}$

Simplify, and combine like terms when possible.

15. $(-8i)(7i)(11i) =$

16. $\left(-3\sqrt{-6}\right)\left(4\sqrt{6}\right) =$

Simplify.

17. $6\sqrt{\dfrac{1}{2}} - \dfrac{9\sqrt{8}}{2} =$

18. $\left(\sqrt[3]{64}\right)^{5/2}$

Solve and check the answer.

19. $\left[\left(2X^2 - 3X - 2\right) \div \left(X^3 - 2X^2\right)\right] \div \left[\left(4X^2 - 12X\right) \div \left(X^2 - 5X + 6\right)\right] =$

Simplify and combine.

20. $\dfrac{10XY^0X}{XY} - \dfrac{4^{-2}Y^2X^{-3}}{4^{-1}X^{-2}YY^0} - \dfrac{2Y^{-1}XX^{-2}}{Y^{-2}}$

Answer the questions.

1. How many terms are in $(X + A)^5$?

2. Expand $(X + A)^5$.

3. How many terms are in $(1/3\ X + 2)^4$?

4. Expand $(1/3\ X + 2)^4$.

5. What is the fourth term of $(X - 2/3)^6$?

6. What is the second term of $(X - 2/3)^6$?

7. What is the third term of $(X - 3)^5$?

8. What is the sixth term of $(X - 3)^5$?

9. Expand $(X - 2A)^2$.

10. Find the binomial root of the trinomial $16X^2 - 24X + 9$.

11. Expand $(X - 10)^3$.

12. Expand $(X + 1/2)^3$.

Simplify so that there are no imaginary numbers or radicals in the denominator.

13. $\dfrac{8\sqrt{11} - 6}{4\sqrt{2} + 3}$

14. $\dfrac{2i}{1 + 9i}$

Simplify, and combine like terms when possible.

15. $(5i)(9i)(12) =$

16. $\left(8\sqrt{-7}\right)\left(9\sqrt{-7}\right) =$

17. $\sqrt{\dfrac{5}{8}} - 2\sqrt{160}$

18. $\left(\sqrt[3]{125}\right)^3$

19. $\dfrac{4X^2 - 1}{2X + 1} \div \dfrac{4X^2 - 4X + 1}{8X}$

20. $4XY^0 + \dfrac{6XY^{-2}}{XY^{-3}} + \dfrac{9X^4Y^5}{X^3}$

Answer the questions.

1. How many terms are in $(X - 4)^5$?

2. Expand $(X - 4)^5$.

3. How many terms are in $(X + 2)^4$?

4. Expand $(X + 2)^4$.

5. What is the fourth term of $(2X + 3)^5$?

6. What is the second term of $(2X + 3)^5$?

7. What is the first term of $(2X + 1)^4$?

8. What is the third term of $(2X + 1)^4$?

9. Expand $(X + A)^2$.

10. Find the binomial root of the trinomial $36X^2 - 6X + 1/4$.

11. Expand $(X + 4/5)^3$.

12. Expand $(3X + 1)^3$.

Simplify so that there are no imaginary numbers or radicals in the denominator.

13. $\dfrac{\sqrt{8}}{5\sqrt{7} - 4}$

14. $\dfrac{-3i}{2 - 11i}$

Simplify, and combine like terms when possible.

15. $(-5i)(6) =$

16. $\left(5\sqrt{-8}\right)\left(-7\sqrt{-2}\right) =$

17. $\sqrt{\dfrac{1}{10}} + 3\sqrt{90}$

18. $\left(\sqrt{81}\right)^{3/2}$

19. $\dfrac{X^2 + 5X + 6}{X^2 - 16} \div \dfrac{X^2 + 6X + 9}{X^2 + 6X + 8}$

20. $\dfrac{12X^3X^2X^{-1}Y^{-2}}{Y^{-7}} + \dfrac{10X^2}{X^{-2}Y^5} + \dfrac{8XXYX^2}{Y^{-2}X^0Y^{-2}}$

You may have studied simple probability in earlier grades. It tells you what chance you have of getting a particular result in a given number of trials.

Permutations tell you how many different possible results there are in a given situation.

Follow the directions.

1. In how many different ways can you arrange the letters A, B, and C? List them below.

If a set of elements can be arranged six different ways, we say it has six permutations. In #1, we were arranging three letters. Using a factorial, this can be expressed as P (permutations) = 3! = $3 \cdot 2 \cdot 1 = 6$.

2. In how many different ways can you arrange the four letters A, B, C, and D? Use a factorial to solve.

Why does this work? Pretend you have five different books to arrange on a shelf. How many different combinations can you make? As you look at the pile of books, you have five different choices for the first book to put on the shelf. After placing the first book, you have four books and four choices left. Continuing, you have three choices left, then two, and finally one. All of your choices together are $5 \cdot 4 \cdot 3 \cdot 2 \cdot 1 = 5! = 120$.

If you have a scientific calculator, check your handbook to see whether it has a key for doing factorials, and find out how to use it. If you do not have a factorial key, you may still use your calculator for multiplication.

3. Mrs. Jones has six children. Some seats in the family van are preferred to others. Assuming the same six seats are used every time, how many different seating arrangements are possible? Use a factorial to solve.

Sometimes we want to choose only some of the possibilities in a given situation. There are eight jelly beans in a bag, each one a different color. If all eight jelly beans are arranged in every possible way, there will be 8! or 40,320 permutations.

Suppose I want only three jelly beans. If I draw them out of the bag one at a time, how many possible color combinations are there? (Note that in permutations, order is always important.) For my first draw, I have eight choices, for my second seven choices, and for the third draw six choices. So, $P = 8 \cdot 7 \cdot 6 = 336$.

The formula looks like this: $\quad {}_nP_r = \dfrac{n!}{(n-r)!}$ The letter n stands for the number of items in the set; in this example, $n = 8$.

The letter r stands for the number of items to be chosen. In our example, $r = 3$. Study the example to see how this works, and why it saves computation.

$$ {}_8P_3 = \frac{8!}{(8-3)!} = \frac{8!}{5!} = \frac{8 \cdot 7 \cdot 6 \cdot \cancel{5} \cdot \cancel{4} \cdot \cancel{3} \cdot \cancel{2} \cdot \cancel{1}}{\cancel{5} \cdot \cancel{4} \cdot \cancel{3} \cdot \cancel{2} \cdot \cancel{1}} = 336 \text{ or } \frac{8 \cdot 7 \cdot 6 \cdot \cancel{5!}}{\cancel{5!}} = 336 $$

4. In how many ways can four people be seated on nine chairs?

5. There are 20 students in the class and 5 openings for class officers. How many possible combinations of students are there?

6. How many different six-digit license plate numbers may be formed from the letters in the alphabet if the five vowels are not used?

Complete the square by finding the last term.

1. $X^2 + 10X +$ _____

2. $X^2 - 8X +$ _____

Complete the square by finding the middle term.

3. $X^2 +$ _____ $+ 4$

4. $A^2 +$ _____ $+ 225$

Solve for X. Complete the square when necessary. Check your work.

5. $X^2 + 2X + 3 = 0$

6. $X^2 - 5X + 4 = 0$

7. $2X^2 + 8X + 2 = 0$

8. $X^2 + 4X - 7 = 0$

9. $3X^2 - 9X + 3 = 0$

10. $X^2 - 2X - 11 = 0$

Complete the square by finding the last term.

1. $x^2 - 3x +$ _____

2. $x^2 + 1/3\, x +$ _____

Complete the square by finding the middle term.

3. $x^2 +$ _____ $+ 1$

4. $y^2 -$ _____ $+ 16/100$

Solve for X. Complete the square when necessary. Check your work.

5. $x^2 + 4x + 16 = 0$

6. $2X^2 - 16X - 4 = 0$

7. $A^2 + 5A + 1/4 = 0$

8. $X^2 + 8X - 10 = 0$

9. $3X^2 + 18X + 3 = 0$

10. $X^2 - 10X + 30 = 0$

Answer the questions.

1. Expand $(2X + 1/3)^2$.

2. Expand $(3X - 4)^2$.

Complete the square by finding the missing term.

3. $X^2 - 6X + \underline{\quad}$

4. $2X^2 + 20X + \underline{\quad}$

Hint for #4: Divide the first and second terms by 2. After finding the missing term, multiply all the terms by 2 to find the final answer.

5. $X^2 + \underline{\quad} + 196$

6. $X^2 - \underline{\quad} + 36/64$

Solve for X. Complete the square when necessary.

7. $X^2 + 10X + 3 = 0$

8. Check the validity of the roots in #7 by placing them in the original equation.

9. $X^2 - 6X - 6 = 0$

10. Check the validity of the roots in #9 by placing them in the original equation.

11. Expand $(1/2 X - 3B)^4$.

12. Expand $(X + 1)^5$.

13. What is the third term of $(2X - 5)^5$?

14. What is the fifth term of $(2X - 5)^5$?

15. Expand $(4X - 6)^3$.

16. Find the cube root of $X^3 + 12X^2 + 48X + 64$.

Put in standard form.

17. $\dfrac{5 - 6\sqrt{-3}}{4i + 7}$

18. $\dfrac{3 - \sqrt{2}}{3 + \sqrt{2}}$

Simplify, and combine like terms when possible.

19. $(12i)\left(\sqrt{-5} - \sqrt{16}\right)$

20. $(i)(i^3)(i^0)$

Answer the questions.

1. Expand $(1/2\,X - 5)^2$.

2. Expand $(2X - 6)^2$.

Complete the square by finding the missing term.

3. $X^2 - 14X +$ ____

4. $X^2 + 16X +$ ____

5. $X^2 +$ ____ $+ 9$

6. $X^2 -$ ____ $+ 64$

Solve for X. Complete the square when necessary.

7. $X^2 - 4X + 5 = 0$

8. Check the validity of the roots in #7 by placing them in the original equation.

9. $X^2 + 12X + 11 = 0$

10. Check the validity of the roots in #9 by placing them in the original equation.

11. Expand $(1/3 \, X + 2)^4$.

12. Expand $(X - 2A)^5$.

13. What is the second term of $(X + 2A)^5$?

14. What is the sixth term of $(X + 2A)^5$?

15. Expand $(2X - 3)^3$.

16. Find the cube root of $X^3 - 9X^2 + 27X - 27$.

Put in standard form.

17. $\dfrac{4\sqrt{-6}}{8i - 9}$

18. $\dfrac{5 + \sqrt{-3}}{5 - \sqrt{-3}}$

Simplify, and combine like terms when possible.

19. $(4i)\left(2i - \sqrt{-9}\right)$

20. $(i^4)(i^4)$

Answer the questions.

1. Expand $(3X - 1/4)^2$.

2. Expand $(X + 11)^2$.

Complete the square by finding the missing term.

3. $X^2 + 8X +$ ____

4. $X^2 + 30X +$ ____

5. $X^2 +$ ____ $+ 36$

6. $4X^2 +$ ____ $+ 9$

Solve for X. Complete the square when necessary.

7. $X^2 - 3X - 9 = 0$

8. Check the validity of the roots in #7 by placing them in the original equation.

9. $2X^2 + 3X - 2 = 0$

10. Check the validity of the roots in #9 by placing them in the original equation.

11. Expand $(X + 2)^5$.

12. Expand $(2X - 1)^4$.

13. What is the third term of $(X - 1)^6$?

14. What is the fourth term of $(X - 1)^6$?

15. Expand $(3X + 1)^3$.

16. Find the cube root of $X^3 + 15X^2 + 75X + 125$.

Put in standard form.

17. $\dfrac{3 - 2\sqrt{-5}}{7i + 2}$

18. $\dfrac{1 + \sqrt{X}}{2 - \sqrt{X}}$

Simplify, and combine like terms when possible.

19. $\left(18i\right)\left(\sqrt{-36} + 7i\right)$

20. $(i^2)(i)(i^3)$

In lesson 10H, we used the formula $_nP_r = \dfrac{n!}{(n-r)!}$ to choose r items out of a set of n items.

If we are choosing all the items in the set, r and n will be the same.

$_5P_5 = \dfrac{5!}{(5-5)!} = \dfrac{5!}{0!}$ To solve this expression, we need to know the value of 0!

The expression 0! tells us how many ways we can arrange zero items or the empty set { }. According to mathematicians, there is only one way to arrange nothing, so 0! = 1.

$$_5P_5 = \dfrac{5!}{(5-5)!} = \dfrac{5!}{0!} = \dfrac{5!}{1} = 5\cdot4\cdot3\cdot2\cdot1 = 120$$

Note: It is not necessary to use the formula when r and n are the same. The example is to show that the formula still works in that case.

We have been doing problems where each item in the set is different. When two or more items in a set are identical, some permutations will look alike. We count only the permutations that are distinct from one another.

Follow the directions.

1. In how many different ways can you arrange the letters in the word *like*? List them below. Is the result 4 factorial?

2. In how many different ways can you arrange the letters in the word *look*? List them below. Is the result still 4 factorial?

The formula to use when some elements are the same is $P = \dfrac{n!}{r!}$, where n is all the items in the set and r is the number of items that are the same.

Number 2 works out like this: $P = \dfrac{4!}{2!} = \dfrac{4\cdot3\cdot\cancel{2!}}{\cancel{2!}} = 12$

3. How many permutations can be made from the letters in the word *sunny*?

4. How many permutations can be made from the digits in 331243?

5. Richard has six hand bells, two of which ring the same tone. If he rings each bell once, how many different six-note melodies can he play?

6. How many permutations can be made from the letters in the word *banana*? The letter *a* occurs three times and the letter *n* occurs two times, so the formula is as shown.

   $$P = \frac{6!}{3! \, 2!} =$$

7. How many permutations can be made from the letters in the word *mathematics*?

8. Jim has 20 fruit trees that he plans to plant in a row along the edge of a field. He has 15 apple trees, 3 peach trees, and 2 cherry trees. How many different arrangements can he make?

Find the roots, using the quadratic formula when necessary.

1. $X^2 + 6X + 2 = 0$

2. $X^2 - 5X + 4 = 0$

3. $3X^2 + 7X - 1 = 0$

4. $A^2 - 10A = 11$

5. $2Q^2 + 2 = 17Q$

6. $5X^2 + 15X + 10 = 0$

7. $1/4 R^2 - 1/2 R + 3/2 = 0$

8. $16X^2 = 2X + 4$

9. $2X^2 + 3X - 8 = 0$

10. $Y^2 = 3/4 Y + 2$

Find the roots, using the quadratic formula when necessary.

1. $8X^2 - X - 3 = 0$

2. $7 = 2X^2 + X$

3. $Q^2 - 6Q + 3 = 0$

4. $2 + 3X + 4X^2 = 0$

5. $P = P^2 - 2$

6. $X^2 + 1/5\,X + 5 = 0$

7. $20X^2 + 40X = 30$

8. $5A^2 + 2A - 1 = 0$

9. $3X^2 = -5X$

10. $AX^2 + BX + C = 0$

Find the roots, using the quadratic formula when necessary.

1. $X^2 - 5X + 6 = 0$

2. $X^2 + 4X + 2 = 0$

3. $X^2 - 3X + 1 = -6X$

4. $X^2 + 4X - 12 = 0$

5. $2X^2 + 2X + 5 = 0$

6. $X^2 + 8X = -16$

Complete the square.

7. $X^2 - 26X +$ _____

8. $2X^2 + 9X +$ _____

9. $X^2 +$ _____ $+ 400$

10. $X^2 -$ _____ $+ 14$

Solve for X. Complete the square when necessary.

11. $X^2 + 1/3 X - 4/3 = 0$

12. Check the answers to #11 by placing them in the original equation.

13. Expand $(X - A)^6$.

14. What is the second term of $(1/2 \, X - 3A)^4$?

15. Expand $(5 - 2A)^3$.

16. Find the cube root of $X^3 - 6X^2Y + 12XY^2 - 8Y^3$.

Put in standard form.

17. $\dfrac{6 + 5i}{3i - 2}$

18. $\dfrac{2 + \sqrt{-49}}{2 - \sqrt{-49}}$

Simplify, and combine like terms when possible.

19. $\dfrac{2}{3 - \sqrt{7}}$

20. $\dfrac{2 + \sqrt{5}}{2\sqrt{5} - 4}$

Find the roots, using the quadratic formula when necessary.

1. $2x^2 - 9X - 7 = 0$

2. $x^2 + 5X - 2 = 0$

3. $3x^2 + 7X + 4 = 0$

4. $x^2 - 6X + 12 = 0$

5. $5x^2 - 3X - 2 = 0$

6. $4x^2 + 1 = 4X$

Complete the square.

7. $x^2 + 5X +$ _____

8. $x^2 - 1/2 X +$ _____

9. $25x^2 +$ _____ $+ 1$

10. $49x^2 -$ _____ $+ 4$

Solve for X. Complete the square when necessary.

11. $x^2 - 12X + 20 = 0$

12. Check the answers to #11 by placing them in the original equation.

13. Expand $(X + 1)^4$.

14. What is the fifth term of $(1/2 \, X - 3A)^4$?

15. Expand $(10 - 1/X)^3$.

16. Find the cube root of $X^3 + 6X^2 + 12X + 8$.

Put in standard form.

17. $\dfrac{4 - 3i}{2i}$

18. $\dfrac{10 + \sqrt{-A}}{10 - \sqrt{-A}}$

Simplify, and combine like terms when possible.

19. $\dfrac{9}{7 + \sqrt{10}}$

20. $\dfrac{4 - \sqrt{6}}{3\sqrt{7} + 5}$

Find the roots, using the quadratic formula when necessary.

1. $X^2 + 2X - 8 = 0$

2. $X^2 - 6X = -8$

3. $2X^2 - 15X + 7 = 0$

4. $3X^2 + 4X = 7$

5. $2 = 5X + X^2$

6. $X^2 + 2X - 15 = 0$

Complete the square.

7. $4X^2 + 28X +$ _____

8. $9X^2 - 36X +$ _____

9. $36X^2 +$ _____ $+ 25$

10. $81X^2 -$ _____ $+ 121$

Solve for X. Complete the square when necessary.

11. $X^2 + 5X - 14 = 0$

12. Check the answers to #11 by placing them in the original equation.

13. Expand $(2X + 1)^5$.

14. What is the third term of $(1/3\ X + 2)^5$?

15. Expand $(X - 3/5)^3$.

16. Find the cube root of $8X^3 + 12X^2 + 6X + 1$.

Put in standard form.

17. $\dfrac{10 + i}{5i}$

18. $\dfrac{10}{5 - \sqrt{8}}$

Simplify, and combine like terms when possible.

19. $\dfrac{2 + 3\sqrt{6}}{1 - \sqrt{6}}$

20. $\dfrac{6 - \sqrt{2}}{10\sqrt{3} - 8}$

You have used the binomial theorem to find the terms when a binomial is raised to a power. Here is another method that uses factorials. It was discovered by a man named Leonard Euler in the 18th century.

The method is based on the version of Pascal's triangle shown below. If you remember that 0! equals one, you can reduce each fraction so that this becomes a regular Pascal's triangle. Also notice that this is similar to the triangle shown in lesson 10 in your instruction manual.

The notation $\binom{n}{r-1}$ is used in this new formula for terms of an expanded binomial. It is read as "n choose r − 1."

$$\frac{0!}{0!\,0!}$$

$$\frac{1!}{0!\,1!} \qquad \frac{1!}{1!\,0!}$$

$$\frac{2!}{0!\,2!} \qquad \frac{2!}{1!\,1!} \qquad \frac{2!}{2!\,0!}$$

$$\frac{3!}{0!\,3!} \qquad \frac{3!}{1!\,2!} \qquad \frac{3!}{2!\,1!} \qquad \frac{3!}{3!\,0!}$$

The formula for the r term of $(a + b)^n$ is $\binom{n}{r-1} a^{n-r+1} b^{r-1}$. The letter n tells you what row of the triangle you are using, and r tells what term in that row is chosen. Remember that we start counting rows with 0. However, we can start counting terms with one because the formula has already subtracted one from r.

This is not as difficult as it looks! Study the examples, and compare what you are doing here to the method you have already learned.

Example 1

Find the second term of $(a + b)^3$ if $n = 3$ and $r = 2$.

Simplify terms.

$$\binom{n}{r-1} a^{n-r+1} b^{r-1} = \binom{3}{2-1} a^{3-2+1} b^{2-1} = \binom{3}{1} a^2 b^1$$

Change n to n!, or in this case, 3 to 3! Look at the second term (counting from one) of row 3 (counting from zero) to find the factorials for the denominator.

$$\frac{3!}{1!\,2!} a^2 b^1$$

Simplify.

$$\frac{3 \cdot \cancel{2!}}{1! \cdot \cancel{2!}} a^2 b^1 = 3a^2 b$$

Notice that the numbers in the factorial form of the denominator are the b and a exponents and that they add to produce the number in the numerator. This is always true, so you do not need to use the triangle.

Example 2

Find the third term of $(a + b)^6$ if $n = 6$ and $r = 3$.

Simplify terms.

$$\left(\begin{array}{c} n \\ r-1 \end{array}\right) a^{n-r+1} b^{r-1} = \left(\begin{array}{c} 6 \\ 3-1 \end{array}\right) a^{6-3+1} b^{3-1} = \left(\begin{array}{c} 6 \\ 2 \end{array}\right) a^4 b^2$$

Change to factorials and simplify.

$$\frac{6!}{2!\ 4!} a^4 b^2 = \frac{6 \cdot 5 \cdot \cancel{4!}}{2 \cdot \cancel{4!}} a^4 b^2 = 15 a^4 b^2$$

Use factorials to find the requested term.

1. Find the fifth term of $(X + Y)^6$.

2. Find the second term of $(A + 2)^4$.

3. Find the third term of $(P + Q)^5$.

4. Find the fourth term of $(2X - 1)^7$.

Tell the nature of each solution by using the discriminant, and then solve to find the exact roots.

Factor when possible.

1. $X^2 + 6X + 9 = 0$

2. $2X^2 + 7X + 3 = 0$

3. $-2X^2 + 3X + 6 = 0$

4. $3X^2 - 2X + 5 = 0$

5. $7X^2 - 3X = 20$

Tell the nature of each solution by using the discriminant, and then solve to find the exact roots.

Factor when possible.

1. $2R^2 = -5R + 3$

2. $1/4\ X^2 + 2X = -4$

3. $11 + 7Y = -6Y^2$

4. $8X^2 + 10X + 2 = 0$

5. $6R^2 - 5R - 3 = 0$

Answer the questions.

1. Tell the nature of the solution to $X^2 + 3X + 1 = 0$ using the discriminant.

2. Solve to find the exact root(s) of #1. Factor when possible.

3. Tell the nature of the solution to $X^2 + 4X = -49$ using the discriminant.

4. Solve to find the exact root(s) of #3. Factor when possible.

5. Tell the nature of the solution to $X^2 - 5X - 9 = 0$ using the discriminant.

6. Solve to find the exact root(s) of #5. Factor when possible.

7. Tell the nature of the solution to $2X^2 + 11X + 12 = 0$ using the discriminant.

8. Solve to find the exact root(s) of #7. Factor when possible.

Find the roots using the quadratic formula.

9. $X^2 - 8X + 8 = 0$

10. $X^2 + 7X + 12 = 0$

Solve for X. Complete the square if necessary.

11. $X^2 - 7X + 1 = 0$

12. Check the answers to #11 by placing them in the original equation.

13. Expand $(1/2 X + 3)^6$.

14. What is the fourth term of $(4X - 1)^4$?

15. Expand $(1/4 X + 1/5)^3$.

16. Find the cube root of $X^3 - 15X^2 + 75X - 125$.

Simplify.

17. $\dfrac{4 - 3\sqrt{5}}{2} \cdot \dfrac{4 + 3\sqrt{5}}{2}$

18. $\dfrac{2 + \dfrac{1}{4}}{2 - \dfrac{1}{4}}$

Solve and check the solution.

19. $\dfrac{X}{5} - \dfrac{7}{2} - \dfrac{X}{6} = 0$

Multiply.

20. $(X - Ai)(X + Ai)$

Answer the questions.

1. Tell the nature of the solution to $X^2 - 2X - 3 = 0$ using the discriminant.

2. Solve to find the exact root(s) of #1. Factor when possible.

3. Tell the nature of the solution to $X^2 - 2X + 5 = 0$ using the discriminant.

4. Solve to find the exact root(s) of #3. Factor when possible.

5. Tell the nature of the solution to $4X^2 - 20X + 25 = 0$ using the discriminant.

6. Solve to find the exact root(s) of #5. Factor when possible.

7. Tell the nature of the solution to $2X^2 - 2X + 5 = 0$ using the discriminant.

8. Solve to find the exact root(s) of #7. Factor when possible.

Find the roots using the quadratic formula.

9. $3X^2 + 6X = -2$

10. $7X^2 + 2X + 1 = 0$

Solve for X. Complete the square if necessary.

11. $X^2 - 6X - 2 = 0$

12. Check the answers to #11 by placing them in the original equation.

13. Expand $(X + A)^4$.

14. What is the second term of $(4X - 1)^6$?

15. Expand $(X - 2/9)^3$.

16. Find the cube root of $27X^3 + 27X^2 + 9X + 1$.

Simplify.

17. $\dfrac{7 + 2\sqrt{X}}{6} \cdot \dfrac{7 - 2\sqrt{X}}{6}$

18. $\dfrac{X - \dfrac{1}{X}}{3 + \dfrac{1}{3}}$

Solve and check the solution.

19. $\dfrac{4X + 1}{3} - 1 = X + \dfrac{3X - 8}{5}$

Multiply.

20. $(2X - 3i)(2X + 3i)$

Answer the questions.

1. Tell the nature of the solution to $3X^2 + 7X + 2 = 0$ using the discriminant.

2. Solve to find the exact root(s) of #1. Factor when possible.

3. Tell the nature of the solution to $2X^2 - 5X + 4 = 0$ using the discriminant.

4. Solve to find the exact root(s) of #3. Factor when possible.

5. Tell the nature of the solution to $4X^2 - 2X + 9 = 0$ using the discriminant.

6. Solve to find the exact root(s) of #5. Factor when possible.

7. Tell the nature of the solution to $2X^2 - 4X - 7 = 0$ using the discriminant.

8. Solve to find the exact root(s) of #7. Factor when possible.

Find the roots using the quadratic formula.

9. $2X^2 + 6X = 3$

10. $5X^2 + 4 = 8X$

Solve for X. Complete the square if necessary.

11. $3X^2 + 8X - 3 = 0$

12. Check the answers to #11 by placing them in the original equation.

13. Expand $(X + 2A)^5$.

14. What is the sixth term of $(X - 4)^6$?

15. Expand $(2X - A)^3$.

16. Find the cube root of $8X^3 + 36X^2Y + 54XY^2 + 27Y^3$.

Simplify.

17. $\dfrac{10 - \sqrt{AX}}{4} \cdot \dfrac{10 + \sqrt{AX}}{4}$

18. $\dfrac{2X^2 - \dfrac{1}{X^2}}{\dfrac{4}{X}}$

Solve and check the solution.

19. $X + 3 - \dfrac{6X - 5}{2} = \dfrac{2X - 7}{6}$

Multiply.

20. $(A + Bi)(A - Bi)$

13H

The degree of an equation is the same as the largest exponent in the equation. The degree of the equation tells you the number of possible solutions. These solutions are not necessarily unique. For example, the equation $X^2 + 4X + 4 = 0$ is a second degree equation. It has two solutions , 2 and 2, but both of them are the same.

When doing word problems, always check to see if each answer makes sense. An answer may be a valid solution to an equation but not a valid real-life answer to the problem.

Example 1

A gardener has a 30 ft x 20 ft garden completely surrounded by a walkway that has a width of X. If the combined area of the walkway and the garden is 1,200 square feet, how wide is the walkway?

$$\text{Area} = (30 + 2X)(20 + 2X)$$
$$= 600 + 100X + 4X^2$$
$$1200 = 4X^2 + 100X + 600$$
$$300 = X^2 + 25X + 150$$

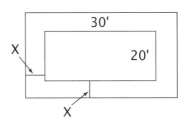

$$X^2 + 25X - 150 = 0$$
$$(X - 5)(X + 30) = 0$$
$$X = 5, \ -30$$

In this case, –30 feet makes no sense, so the walkway is 5 feet wide.

Make a drawing to help you visualize each word problem, and use factoring to help you solve it. Be sure to check each solution to see whether it is a valid real-life answer.

1. A rectangular garden was fenced using an existing fence on one side. The remaining three sides required 20 feet of fencing material. The area of the enclosed garden was 48 square feet. Find all possible dimensions for the garden.

2. Mr. Smith built a fence to divide his rectangular backyard into two regions. There was fencing on all four sides and a fence parallel to two of the sides that divided the yard into the two regions. Mr. Smith used 160 feet of fencing, and the entire fenced area of the backyard was 1,000 square feet. Find all possible dimensions for the entire fenced area.

3. The height of a triangle is two inches more than the width. The area is 24 square inches. What is the height of the triangle?

4. The length of a rectangle is four inches more than the width. The area is 192 square inches. How wide is the rectangle?

Answer the questions.

1. The original price of the book was $45.00. Sarah bought it on sale for $33.75. What percent of the original price did she save?

2. The wholesale price of a shirt is $15.00 and the retail price is $25.00. What percent of the wholesale price is the markup or profit?

3. If the wholesale price of the shirt is $15.00 and the retail price is $25.00, what percent of the retail price is the profit?

4. The wholesale price of the chair was $32.00. The retail cost included a markup of 28%. What was the final cost of the chair?

5. The used car sold for $2,500. The dealer made a profit of 15% of the original cost. What was the original cost? (Round to the nearest dollar.)

6. In March, winter coats were advertised for 55% off the marked price. What would Naomi pay for a coat that was marked $195.00?

7. The state sales tax is 6%. Grace paid a total of $32.45 at the check-out. What was the amount of her purchase before taxes? (Round to the nearest cent.)

8. The price of the food at the restaurant came to $45.50. If the tax was 5.4% of that amount and the tip was 15%, what was the total amount spent? (Round to the nearest cent.)

For #9–12, use the atomic weight table in the instruction manual or on the symbols and tables page at the back of this book. Round to the nearest whole percent.

9. Find the percentage of silicon in SiO_2.

10. Find the percentage of oxygen in SiO_2.

11. Find the percentage of iron in Fe_2O_3.

12. Find the percentage of oxygen in Fe_2O_3.

Answer the questions.

1. The grocery store marked up all of its canned goods by 13%. What is the retail price of an item whose wholesale price is $.59?

2. Arthur earned $8,500 with his home business. Self-employment tax is 15.3%. How much tax must he pay?

3. The price of Tom's meal was $13.50, but the bill said $14.04. What percent was the meal tax?

4. The waitress gave Tom special assistance, so he gave a 20% tip. How much was his tip? (Figure the tip on the before-tax amount.)

5. The wholesale price of the paint is $9.50 and the retail price is $15.00. What percent of the retail price is the markup?

6. Forecasters predicted that the price of gasoline would rise by 12% over the summer. If the current price of a gallon is $1.38, what is the predicted price (to nearest cent)?

7. The total cost of new living room furniture was $955.00. This included a 4.5% sales tax and a 7% delivery fee. What was the price of the furniture, the amount of the tax, and the amount of the delivery fee?

8. All of the items on the sale rack were discounted 45%. What will Ruth pay for a dress marked $75?

For #9–12, use the atomic weight table in the instruction manual or at the back of this book. Round to the nearest whole percent.

9. Find the percentage of potassium in $K_2Cr_2O_7$.

10. Find the percentage of chromium in $K_2Cr_2O_7$.

11. Find the percentage of sodium in NaOH.

12. Find the percentage of hydrogen in NaOH.

For #1–2: Joe's Warehouse pays a wholesale price of $4.00 for every CD it purchases. They are resold for $9.50.

1. What percent of the wholesale price is the profit?

2. What percent of the retail price is the profit?

For #3–4: The young accountant made $23,600 this year.

3. If the state income tax is 6.2%, how much does he fork over this year?

4. He learned that he would also have to pay 7.65% into FICA. How much is his contribution?

5. After a delicious dinner, the bill came to $28.50. How much is the 15% tip?

6. The tax on the dinner is 8 1/4%. What is the amount of the tax?

For #7–8, use the atomic weight table in the instruction manual or at the back of this book.

7. Find the percentage of carbon in CS_2.

8. Find the percentage of sulfur in CS_2.

9. Tell the nature of the solution to $2X^2 + 8X + 8 = 0$ by using the discriminant.

10. Solve to find the exact root(s) of #9. Factor when possible.

11. Tell the nature of the solution to $X^2 - 5X - 7 = 0$ by using the discriminant.

12. Solve to find the exact root(s) of #11. Factor when possible.

13. Tell the nature of the solution to $X^2 + 4X + 6 = 0$ by using the discriminant.

14. Solve to find the exact root(s) of #13. Factor when possible.

Find the roots using the quadratic formula.

15. $2X^2 - 1 = -3X$

16. $X^2 + 5 = 5X$

Solve for X. Complete the square if necessary.

17. $X^2 + 4X = 32$

18. Check the answers to #17 by placing them in the original equation.

19. Expand $(X - 1)^5$.

20. What is the fourth term of $(X + 3)^4$?

For #1–3: Working at the Slacks' Emporium, Sam noticed that slacks were purchased from the wholesaler for $12.50, and then marked up and resold for $19.95.

1. What percent of the wholesale price is the profit?

2. What percent of the retail price is the profit?

3. What percent of the retail is the wholesale?

For #4–6: The bill for the food at the swanky diner was $78.10.

4. What is the tax if the rate is 5.50%?

5. How much is the 15% tip?

6. What percent of the final money spent for the evening is the tax and tip combined?

For #7–8, use the atomic weight table in the instruction manual or at the back of this book.

7. Find the percentage of hydrogen in H_2S.

8. Find the percentage of sulfur in H_2S.

9. Tell the nature of the solution to $4X^2 + 8X + 20 = 0$ by using the discriminant.

10. Solve to find the exact root(s) of #9. Factor when possible.

11. Tell the nature of the solution to $2X^2 - 7X = -4$ by using the discriminant.

12. Solve to find the exact root(s) of #11. Factor when possible.

13. Tell the nature of the solution to $3X^2 = 7X + 4$ by using the discriminant.

14. Solve to find the exact root(s) of #13. Factor when possible.

Find the roots using the quadratic formula.

15. $6X^2 - 5X = 0$

16. $5X^2 - 4 = 0$

Solve for X. Complete the square if necessary.

17. $5X^2 + 4X = 0$

18. Check the answers to #17 by placing them in the original equation.

19. Expand $(X - 2A)^5$.

20. What is the third term of $(X + 3)^4$?

For #1–3: At the clearance sale, David observed that every item in the store was being discounted 60%.

1. How much is the $149.95 power saw after the discount?

2. How much is the $399.00 lawn mower after the discount?

3. How much is the $21.90 rake after the discount?

For #4–6: The bill for the food at the diner was $54.45.

4. What is the tax if the rate is 7.25%?

5. How much would a 16% tip cost?

6. What percent of the final money spent for the evening is the tax and tip combined?

For #7–8, use the atomic weight table in the instruction manual or at the back of this book.

7. Find the percentage of carbon in CH_4.

8. Find the percentage of hydrogen in CH_4.

9. Tell the nature of the solution to $X^2 + 3X - 5 = 0$ by using the discriminant.

10. Solve to find the exact root(s) of #9. Factor when possible.

11. Tell the nature of the solution to $3X^2 = X + 3$ by using the discriminant.

12. Solve to find the exact root(s) of #11. Factor when possible.

13. Tell the nature of the solution to $3X^2 - 5X = -2$ by using the discriminant.

14. Solve to find the exact root(s) of #13. Factor when possible.

Find the roots using the quadratic formula.

15. $4X^2 + 7X = 2$

16. $3X^2 + 5 = 8X$

Solve for X. Complete the square if necessary.

17. $X^2 - 8X + 9 = 0$

18. Check the answers to #17 by placing them in the original equation.

19. Expand $(2X - 1)^5$.

20. What is the sixth term of $(2X - 3)^5$?

Sometimes word problems ask for the **percent** or **rate** of increase or decrease. To solve these problems, you must first find the **amount** of increase or decrease. Other problems require you to find the amount of increase or decrease, and then add it to or subtract it from the starting amount.

Read and solve. The first one is done for you.

1. Five years ago, a house was worth $95,000. It is now valued at $120,000. What is the percent of increase over the value five years ago?

   Solution: 120,000 − 95,000 = $25,000 increase

   $$25,000 = WP \times 95,000$$
   $$25,000 \div 95,000 = WP$$
   $$WP = .26 \text{ or } 26\% \text{ (rounded)}$$

2. Another house was worth $145,000 five years ago. If its value increased by the same percent as in #1, what is the current value of the house?

3. During January sales, a store sold a $150 coat for 25% less than in December. What is the difference between the December and January price of the coat? What is the new price of the coat?

4. A farmer found that if he fertilized his fields, crop yields would increase by 29%. His original yield was 28.5 bushels per acre. The cost of applying fertilizer was $25 per acre. If he is able to sell his crop for $4.15 per bushel, how much more will the farmer make per acre by using fertilizer?

5. If the farmer in #4 plants 150 acres of the crop in question, what is the total increase in income generated by using fertilizer? What percent of increase is this over the income he would have earned without fertilizer? (Note that this is not all profit, as we have not figured expenses other than fertilizer.)

6. Last year, Linda sold $20,578 worth of books (retail sales). This year her retail sales jumped to $29,352. What was the percent of increase in her retail sales? If her sales increase by the same percent next year, what amount can Linda expect in retail sales next year?

7. Tim took a course in efficient driving. Before the course, he used 4.7 gallons of gasoline for every 100 miles he drove. After taking the course, he used only 4.1 gallons to travel 100 miles. How many gallons did he save every 100 miles? This saving is what percent of the amount of fuel he used before taking the course?

8. Gasoline costs $1.98 per gallon. How much money will Tim save on a 600-mile trip after taking the course?

9. The population of our town is 400% of what it was 30 years ago, when it was 20,567. What is the current population of our town?

10. What was the percent of increase of the population of the town in #9 in 30 years?

Follow the directions.

1. Solve for A. $AFG = H$

2. Solve for B. $AB = GF$

3. Solve for X. $\dfrac{X}{YZ} = \dfrac{P}{Q}$

4. Solve for Y. $\dfrac{X}{YZ} = \dfrac{A}{B}$

5. Solve for A. $C - A = D + B$

6. Solve for X. $X + Y + Z = B + A$

7. Solve for B. $\dfrac{B}{C+D} = 0$

8. Solve for G. $G(A + B) = D$

9. Solve for Y. $\dfrac{1}{Y} = \dfrac{X}{Z}$

10. Solve for R. $Q = RS + RT$

11. Solve for X. $R = \dfrac{2}{3}X + Y$

12. Solve for π. $B = 2\pi r h$

Follow the directions.

1. Solve for X. $\dfrac{1}{Y} = \dfrac{1}{X} + \dfrac{1}{Z}$

2. Solve for B^2. $\dfrac{B_1}{A_2} = \dfrac{A_1}{B_2}$

3. Solve for W. $R = BW(1 + X)$

4. Solve for A. $2A = \dfrac{1}{2}A + B$

5. Solve for X. $XYZ = YZQ$

6. Solve for Y. $X = \dfrac{XY}{4}$

7. Solve for T. $D = RT$

8. Solve for X. $TS = XT + XS$

9. Solve for B. $3 - \dfrac{A}{B} = C$

10. Solve for P. $Q(P + R) - S = 10$

11. Solve for X. $AX + BX + CX = D$

12. Solve for i. $X = \dfrac{Y}{W + i}$

Follow the directions.

1. Solve for B. $\dfrac{B}{C} = \dfrac{A}{D}$

2. Solve for R. $D = RT$

3. Solve for X. $\dfrac{AB}{C} = \dfrac{Y}{X}$

4. Solve for A. $\dfrac{1}{A} = \dfrac{B}{C}$

5. Solve for T. $D = RT$

6. Solve for D. $\dfrac{A}{B} - \dfrac{D}{E} = 0$

7. Every item on the rack has been marked up 40% of the retail price. If the jacket sells for $59.00 retail, what is the original wholesale price?

8. What percentage of the wholesale price is the profit in #7?

9. After a satisfying evening, the bill came to the table. The total was $62.30. How much should the 15% tip be?

10. If the total for #9 after the tip and tax had been included was $76.15, what is the tax rate?

For #11–12, use the atomic weight table in the instruction manual or at the back of this book. Continue to round your answers for this kind of problem to the nearest whole percent.

11. Find the percentage of carbon in H_2CO.

12. Find the percentage of oxygen in H_2CO.

13. Tell the nature of the solution to $X^2 + 9X + 20 = 0$ by using the discriminant.

14. Solve to find the exact root(s) of #13. Factor when possible.

15. Tell the nature of the solution to $X^2 - 25 = 0$ by using the discriminant.

16. Solve to find the exact root(s) of #15. Factor when possible.

Find the roots using the quadratic formula.

17. $9X^2 + 3X = 2$

18. $3X^2 - 15X - 42 = 0$

Solve for X. Complete the square if necessary.

19. $4X^2 - X - 4 = 0$

20. Check the answers to #19 by placing them in the original equation.

Follow the directions.

1. Solve for H.   V = LWH

2. Solve for B. $A = \dfrac{AB}{2}$

3. Solve for L.   P = 2L + 2W

4. Solve for H. $V = \pi R^2 H$

5. Solve for R.   A = 2πRH

6. Solve for R. $I = \dfrac{E}{R + r}$

7. After deducting 15.3% for self-employment tax and 3% for state tax, I took home $968.40 for two weeks' work. What was my gross pay?

8. If I work 90-hour weeks (#7), what is my hourly rate of pay?

9. If I receive a 12% raise in my hourly rate (#8), what is my new take-home pay for two weeks?

10. What is the gross pay from which you figured the take-home pay in #9?

For #11–12, use the atomic weight table.

11. Find the percentage of lithium in Li_2SO_3.

12. Find the percentage of sulfur in Li_2SO_3.

13. Tell the nature of the solution to $X^2 - 4X + 13 = 0$ by using the discriminant.

14. Solve to find the exact root(s) of #13. Factor when possible.

15. Tell the nature of the solution to $X^2 + 6X = 3$ by using the discriminant.

16. Solve to find the exact root(s) of #15. Factor when possible.

Find the roots using the quadratic formula.

17. $2X^2 + 6X = 3$

18. $2X^2 + 13X = 2X$

Simplify.

19. $\dfrac{4X^2Y^{-3}}{12A^3Y^{-1}} \cdot \dfrac{7AX^2}{A^{-2}} \cdot \dfrac{9AY^2}{14X^{-2}A}$

20. $\dfrac{8A^2X}{132X^{-2}} \cdot \dfrac{12X^{-2}A}{11X^3A^{-2}}$

Follow the directions.

1. Solve for C. $F = \dfrac{9}{5}C + 32$

2. Solve for W_2. $\dfrac{W_1}{W_2} = \dfrac{L_2}{L_1}$

3. Solve for H. $A = 2\pi r (H + r)$

4. Solve for A. $\dfrac{1}{F} = \dfrac{1}{A} - \dfrac{1}{B}$

5. Solve for M_1. $F = K\dfrac{M_1 M_2}{D_2}$

6. Solve for π. $A = 2\pi r h$

7. In '97 the Orioles were 56 (wins) and 25 (losses) at the halfway point in the season. What percent of the total games played were wins?

8. What percent of the games played were losses (#7)?

9. The Orioles finished with a won/lost record of 105-57. How many games were won in the second half? (See #7.)

10. What was the team's winning percentage in the second half of the season (#9)?

For #11–12, use the atomic weight table.

11. Find the percentage of nitrogen in NH_3.

12. Find the percentage of hydrogen in NH_3.

13. Tell the nature of the solution to $3X^2 - 7X + 2 = 0$ by using the discriminant.

14. Solve to find the exact root(s) of #13. Factor when possible.

15. Tell the nature of the solution to $5X^2 = 45$ by using the discriminant.

16. Solve to find the exact root(s) of #15. Factor when possible.

Find the roots using the quadratic formula.

17. $3X^2 + 2X = 0$ 18. $4X^2 + 3 = 12X$

Solve for X.

19. $\dfrac{2X + 1}{5} - X = \dfrac{4 - 3X}{4} - 2$ 20. $\dfrac{4X}{9} - 1 = \dfrac{-5X}{12} + X$

Sometimes it is convenient to isolate a variable in a formula before you begin to solve it. If you will be finding the same unknown in several problems, rearrange the formula or equation so that the letter that represents the desired information stands alone on one side of the equation.

Example 1

$$d = rt$$

The letter d equals distance, r equals rate of travel, and t equals time. If rate and time are known, distance is easily found. Suppose that you know distance and time, and need to find the rate for a number of examples. Solve the equation for r just as you would solve for the unknown.

Divide both sides by t.

$$\frac{d}{t} = \frac{rt}{t}$$

$$\frac{d}{t} = r \quad \text{or} \quad r = \frac{d}{t}$$

Now you can easily find rate when distance and time are known.

Sometimes several steps are necessary in order to isolate the variable. Remember and apply all the skills you have learned in solving for the unknown.

Isolate the variable requested for each formula. You will use some of these formulas in science classes.

1. Solve for f. $E = hf$

2. Solve for A. $P = \dfrac{F}{A}$

3. Solve for W. $P = 2L + 2W$

4. Solve for P. $k = \dfrac{PV}{T}$

5. Solve for a. $N = \dfrac{a+b}{2}$

6. Solve for c. $M = \dfrac{a+b}{c+d}$

7. If you drive a car, the formula d = rt shows the relationship between the distance you drive, the rate of speed at which you drive, and the time that you drive. Suppose that the time you spend on the road stays the same and your rate of speed increases. Will the value of *d* increase, decrease, or stay the same? Use numbers in place of the letters to show that your answer makes sense.

8. Now suppose that the value of t decreases and the value of *r* remains the same. Will the value of *d* increase, decrease, or stay the same? Again, use numbers to illustrate your answer.

Given: $R = \dfrac{E}{i}$

9. Explain how the value of *R* will change as the value of *E* increases and the value of *i* remains the same.

10. Explain how the value of *R* will change as the value of *i* increases and the value of *E* remains the same.

For each question, list all the possible equations, and then use the best one to find the answer.

1. The ratio of apples to oranges used in the salad was six to five. If 12 apples were used, how many oranges were needed?

2. There are 30 days in the month of September. If the ratio of cloudy to sunny days was one to two, how many days were cloudy and how many were sunny?

3. A total of 490,000 votes was cast. The ratio of votes received by Candidate A and by Candidate B was two to five. How many votes did candidate B receive?

4. Squirrels outnumber rabbits by a ratio of eight to seven. If 56 rabbits are present, how many squirrels are there?

5. Mrs. Smith's class has 24 students. The ratio of students who like reading best to those who like math best is three to five. How many like math best?

For #6–10, use the atomic weight tables. Round to nearest hundredth.

6. There are 406 grams of NaCl. What is the mass of the sodium?

7. What is the mass of chlorine in 406 grams of NaCl?

8. There are 352 grams of H_2CO_2. What is the mass of the hydrogen?

9. What is the mass of carbon in 352 grams of H_2CO_2?

10. What is the mass of oxygen in 352 grams of H_2CO_2?

For each question, list all the possible equations, and then use the best one to find the answer.

1. The ratio of the fertilizer was five parts nitrogen to ten parts all other ingredients. The farmer bought 135 pounds of fertilizer. How many pounds of nitrogen did he get?

2. The ratio of high school students who were home schooled to those who attended other schools was three to seven. If there were 90 home schoolers, what was the total number of high school students?

3. The ratio of time Mary spends on sports compared to school work is two to three. If she spends four hours a day practicing sports, how many hours does she spend studying?

4. The chosen color was three parts forest green to one part antique ivory. Julia needs eight gallons of paint to do the job. How many quarts of each color should she buy to do the job?

5. The ratio of average snowfall in the two towns is four to five. If the first town usually gets 22 inches a year, what is the average snowfall in the second town?

For #6–10, use the atomic weight tables.

6. There are 480 grams of CF_2Cl_2. What is the mass of the carbon?

7. What is the mass of fluorine in 480 grams of CF_2Cl_2?

8. What is the mass of chlorine in 480 grams of CF_2Cl_2?

9. There are 550 grams of K_2S. What is the mass of the potassium?

10. What is the mass of sulfur in 550 grams of K_2S?

For #1–3: A Sunday School class has 21 students. As the teacher took roll, he noticed that the boys out-numbered the girls by a four to three ratio. How many boys were present?

1. List all the possible equations.

2. Tell which one will be used, and why.

3. Solve.

For #4–6: Carbon and hydrogen are present in 234 grams of C_2H_2.

4. List all the possible equations.

5. What is the mass of the carbon?

6. What is the mass of the hydrogen?

For #7–9: Iron and chlorine are present in 805 grams of $FeCl_3$.

7. List all the possible equations.

8. What is the mass of the iron?

9. What is the mass of the chlorine?

10. Solve for Z. $\dfrac{Y}{Z} = X$

11. Solve for T. $\dfrac{R}{S} = \dfrac{T}{QW}$

12. Mike Mussina's won/lost record is 13-5. What percentage of the games did he win?

13. What percentage of the games did he lose (#12)?

For #14–16, use the atomic weight table. Round answers to the nearest whole percent.

14. Find the percentage of carbon in CF_2Cl_2.

15. Find the percentage of fluorine in CF_2Cl_2.

16. Find the percentage of chlorine in CF_2Cl_2.

17. Tell the nature of the solution to $2X^2 + X = -1/2$ using the discriminant.

18. Solve to find the exact root(s) of #17. Factor when possible.

Solve for X. Complete the square if necessary.

19. $X^2 + 7/4 X = 1/2$

20. Check the answers to #19 by placing them in the original equation.

For #1–3: Davey's Restaurant did a survey and discovered that its customers preferred orange juice to cranberry juice by a four to three ratio. If 165 preferred cranberry juice, how many customers were interviewed?

1. List all the possible equations.

2. Tell which one will be used, and why.

3. Solve.

For #4–6: Potassium and oxygen are present in 752 grams of K_2O.

4. List all the possible equations.

5. What is the mass of the potassium?

6. What is the mass of the oxygen?

For #7–9: Carbon, hydrogen, and fluorine are present in 840 grams of CHF_3.

7. List some possible equations.

8. What is the mass of the carbon?

9. What is the mass of the fluorine?

10. Solve for H. $r = \frac{1}{3}\pi r^2 H$

11. Solve for N. $S = N \times \frac{A+L}{T}$

For #12–13: Before the battle, 1,650 Marines established a beachhead. Only 932 Marines remained after the battle.

12. What percentage of the original company remained?

13. What percentage were killed or missing in action?

For #14–16, use the atomic weight table. Round answers to the nearest whole percent.

14. Find the percentage of carbon in H_2CO.

15. Find the percentage of hydrogen in H_2CO.

16. Find the percentage of oxygen in H_2CO.

17. Tell the nature of the solution to $X^2 + 16 = -8X$ using the discriminant

18. Solve to find the exact root(s) of #17. Factor when possible.

Solve for X.

19. $\dfrac{8X-3}{6} + 1 = \dfrac{X-5}{3} - \dfrac{2-3X}{8}$

20. $\dfrac{3X}{7} - X = \dfrac{5X}{3} - 2$

For #1–3: Fans at the stadium preferred football to soccer by three to one. If 11,300 fans liked soccer, how many were at the stadium?

1. List all the possible equations.

2. Tell which one will be used, and why.

3. Solve.

For #4–6: Sulfur and hydrogen are present in 442 grams of H_2S.

4. List all the possible equations.

5. What is the mass of the sulfur?

6. What is the mass of the hydrogen?

For #7–9: Iron and nitrogen are present in 882 grams of NFe_2.

7. List all the possible equations.

8. What is the mass of the iron?

9. What is the mass of the nitrogen?

10. Solve for F. $\dfrac{1}{F} = \dfrac{1}{A} + \dfrac{1}{B}$

11. Solve for E. $\dfrac{AB}{XY} + \dfrac{CD}{E} = 0$

For #12–13: One night 5,435,960 Israelites left Egypt through the Red Sea. 45% of them were male.

12. How many men were there?

13. What is the ratio of women to men?

For #14–16, use the atomic weight table. Round answers to the nearest whole percent.

14. Find the percentage of sodium in NaOH.

15. Find the percentage of oxygen in NaOH.

16. Find the percentage of hydrogen in NaOH.

17. Tell the nature of the solution to $X^2 - 2/3X = 4/3$ using the discriminant.

18. Solve to find the exact root(s) of #17. Factor when possible.

Solve for X.

19. $3^2 - X = 1.25X - 8.4$

20. $\dfrac{X}{2} + 15 = \dfrac{X}{3} + X$

16H

Gears are used in machines to change the direction of motion. Gears of different sizes can also change the speed of one part of a machine in relation to another part. You can see examples of gears in a bicycle, an old-fashioned watch or clock, or a sewing machine. (Ask permission before unscrewing the top or bottom plate of a sewing machine to look at the gears.)

Follow the directions to learn more about gears.

1. The large gear shown on the right has 12 teeth. The smaller gear has 6 teeth. The larger gear is connected to a power source that turns it at 120 revolutions per minute (rpm). Do you think the smaller gear will turn more slowly or more quickly than the large gear? Hint: Think about how many times the small gear will turn each time the large gear goes around once. Is it more or less than one time?

2. Here is a formula, or equation, that shows the relationship between the number of teeth on two different gears and the speed at which each gear turns:

   $$RN = rn.$$

   The letter N represents the number of teeth on the larger gear and lowercase n is the number of teeth on the smaller gear. The letter R is the number of revolutions per minute of the larger gear and r represents the rpm of the smaller gear. Substitute the data from #1 above and solve to find the rpm of the smaller gear.

3. Here is one way to write the relationship as a ratio: $\dfrac{R}{r} = \dfrac{n}{N}$

   Can you show that this is the same as the formula given in #2?

4. It is useful to be able to write a formula in different ways in order to make it more efficient to find the desired information. Write four versions of the gear formula, each one isolating a different unknown. You may start with the version in #2 or the version in number #3.

For each question, choose one of the formulas you wrote in #4.

5. One gear has 40 teeth and another has 30 teeth. The larger gear is turning at 300 rpm. What is the speed (rpm) of the smaller gear?

6. A gear with 55 teeth is turning at 150 rpm. It is connected to a larger gear that is moving at only 50 rpm. How many teeth does the larger gear have?

7. A large gear has 90 teeth and a smaller gear has 60 teeth. The smaller gear is turning at 600 rpm. What is the speed of the larger gear?

Sometimes gear wheels do not touch each other. Instead of being moved by teeth, they have a belt that goes around both wheels. The ratios work the same way, but instead of using the number of teeth, the formula uses the diameters of each of the wheels. The equation looks like this: RD = rd.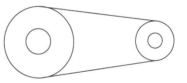

8. A large wheel has a diameter of 10 inches and a speed of 2,000 rpm. It is connected by a belt to a smaller wheel. What should the diameter of the smaller wheel be if the designer wants it to turn at 4,000 rpm?

Gear ratios have many applications in the family car. If you are interested, get someone knowledgeable to explain these applications to you.

Use unit multipliers to change the units of measure.

1. 156 inches = _____ feet

2. 8 pounds = _____ ounces

3. 7 centimeters = _____ meters

4. 15 inches^2 = _____ feet^2

5. 25 gallons = _____ pints

6. 10 miles^2 = _____ feet^2

Use unit multipliers to change from imperial to metric or metric to imperial measure. Use the conversion tables at the back of this book if needed.

7. 13 ounces = _____ grams

8. 9 liters = _____ quarts

9. 350 centimeters = _____ inches

10. 17 yards = _____ meters

11. 4 kilometers = _____ feet

12. 50 gallons = _____ liters

Use unit multipliers to change the units of measure.

1. 7 miles = _____ feet

2. 6,342 pounds = _____ tons

3. 7,040 yards = _____ miles

4. 852 feet^2 = _____ inches^2

5. 95 kilometers^2 = _____ meters^2

6. 580 grams = _____ kilograms

Use unit multipliers to change from imperial to metric or metric to imperial measure. Use the conversion tables at the back of this book if needed.

7. 87 inches = _____ meters

8. 106 miles = _____ kilometers

9. 45 kilograms = _____ ounces

10. 9 pounds = _____ grams

11. 3 liters = _____ pints

12. 14 kilograms = _____ pounds

Use unit multipliers to change the units of measure.

1. 3 tons = _____ ounces

2. 24 pints = _____ gallons

3. 5 yards^2 = _____ feet^2

4. 2 feet^3 = _____ yards^3

5. 4 miles^2 = _____ yards^2

Use unit multipliers to convert from imperial to metric or metric to imperial measure.

6. 10 miles = _____ kilometers

7. 25 ounces = _____ grams

8. 5 pounds = _____ kilograms

9. 20 meters = _____ yards

10. 12 liters = _____ quarts

For #11–13: Hydrogen and oxygen are present in 234 grams of H_2O.

11. List all the possible equations.

12. What is the mass of the oxygen?

13. What is the mass of the hydrogen?

For #14–16: On a one-acre lot in south Georgia, the ratio of pecan trees to oak trees was seven to two. If there were 36 trees on the property, how many were pecan trees?

14. List all the possible ratios.

15. Tell which one will be used, and why.

16. Solve.

17. Solve for X. $\dfrac{1}{X} = \dfrac{2Y}{3} + A$

18. Solve for C. $\dfrac{A}{C} = 5 - \dfrac{1}{B}$

For #19–20, use the atomic weight table.

19. Find the percentage of oxygen in MgO.

20. Find the percentage of magnesium in MgO.

SYSTEMATIC REVIEW

Use unit multipliers to change the units of measure.

1. 65 yards = _____ inches

2. 10.6 meters = _____ kilometers

3. 50 feet^2 = _____ yards^2

4. 1,860 inches^3 = _____ yards^3

5. 4 centimeters^2 = _____ meters^2

Use unit multipliers to convert from imperial to metric or metric to imperial measure.

6. 45 inches = _____ centimeters

7. 7 quarts = _____ liters

8. 200 centimeters = _____ inches

9. 3 kilometers = _____ feet

10. 9 kilograms = _____ pounds

For #11–13: Hydrogen and chlorine are present in 612 grams of HCl.

11. List all the possible equations.

12. What is the mass of the chlorine?

13. What is the mass of the hydrogen?

For #14–16: During the overcast winter, the ratio of sunny days to dreary days was two to five. If there were 32 sunny days, how many dreary days were there?

14. List all the possible ratios.

15. Tell which one will be used, and why.

16. Solve.

17. Solve for A. $\dfrac{A}{a} = \dfrac{B}{b}$

18. Solve for a. $\dfrac{A}{a} = \dfrac{B}{b}$

For #19–20, use the atomic weight table.

19. Find the percentage of oxygen in CO_2.

20. Find the percentage of carbon in CO_2.

Use unit multipliers to change the units of measure.

1. 28 feet = _____ inches

2. .28 kilometers = _____ meters

3. 8,000 yards^2 = _____ miles^2

4. 39 kilometers^3 = _____ meters^3

5. 4.8 meters^2 = _____ millimeters^2

Use unit multipliers to convert from imperial to metric or metric to imperial measure.

6. 12 yards = _____ meters

7. 10,000 feet = _____ kilometers

8. 3 pounds = _____ grams

9. 36 meters = _____ feet

10. 340 grams = _____ ounces

For #11–13: Hydrogen and carbon are present in 208 grams of CH_4.

11. List all the possible equations.

12. What is the mass of the carbon?

13. What is the mass of the hydrogen?

For #14–16: The mailman noticed that many people on his route decorated their homes for Christmas. The ratio of decorated to those that were not decorated was seven to five. If 35 homes were not decorated, how many were decorated?

14. List all the possible ratios.

15. Tell which one will be used, and why.

16. Solve.

17. Solve for X. $Y = X (A - B)$

18. Solve for B. $Y = X (A - B)$

For #19–20, use the atomic weight table.

19. Find the percentage of oxygen in H_2O.

20. Find the percentage of hydrogen in H_2O.

Here is a trick for doing one kind of challenging factoring problem.

Example 1

$$x^4 + 3x^2 + 2$$

This problem looks strangely suspicious. It would factor perfectly if it were $x^2 + 3x + 2$. The solution is to make a substitution. Let $W = x^2$.

$W^2 + 3W + 2$ substituting W for x^2

$(W + 1)(W + 2)$ factoring

$(x^2 + 1)(x^2 + 2)$ substituting x^2 back into the expression

Use substitution to factor.

1. $x^4 + 3x^2 - 10$ Let $W = x^2$.

2. $x^4 - 8x^2 + 12$ Let $W = x^2$.

3. $x + 3\sqrt{x} + 2$ Let $W = \sqrt{x}$.

You have had quite a bit of experience in simplifying rational expressions, but some may still seem confusing.

Example 2

What would you do to simplify $\dfrac{X-1}{1-X}$?

You can reverse the terms in either the numerator or the denominator, and then multiply by –1 to keep the original value.

$$\frac{(-1)(1-X)}{(1-X)}$$

Notice carefully that you have not changed the value of the numerator.

Now cancel like terms. The answer is –1.

$$\frac{(-1)\cancel{(1-X)}}{\cancel{(1-X)}} = -1$$

Use factoring and the (–1) principle shown above to simplify the following expressions.

4. $\dfrac{X-2}{-X^2+3X-2} =$

5. $\dfrac{3-X}{X^2-9} =$

6. $\dfrac{X^2-4}{2-X} \cdot \dfrac{X+3}{9-X^2} =$

Use the distance formula to solve these motion problems.

1. Shane drove at 45 miles per hour for 4 hours. How far did he drive?

2. The tortoise covered a distance of 36 yards in 72 minutes. What was his rate of travel?

3. The hare could travel at a rate of 12 yards a minute. How long would it have taken him to cover the 36-yard course if he had not stopped to rest?

Draw diagrams for #4-6 before solving.

4. Bob and Sue both left at 6:00 a.m. to drive to Pennsylvania. Bob drove at an average speed of 60 mph and arrived at 3:00 p.m. Sue's speed averaged 10 miles an hour slower. When did Sue arrive?

5. Two trains were scheduled between Lancaster and Philadelphia. One train averaged 45 mph and the other made more stops and averaged only 35 mph. The second train took .4 of an hour longer to make the run. How far is it between the stations?

6. Gerry left at 4:00 p.m. traveling at 55 mph. Joe left one hour later and passed Gerry at 9:00 p.m. How fast was Joe traveling?

Use the distance formula to solve these motion problems.

1. Shayla covered a distance of 336 miles in 6 hours. What was her rate of travel?

2. Kim can walk at an average rate of 3.5 miles an hour. How long will it take her to walk 21 miles?

3. The sloth traveled at a rate of 4 1/2 feet a minute for 2 hours. How far did it travel?

Draw diagrams for #4-6 before solving.

4. It took Alisha 18 minutes to drive to work at a rate of 50 mph. Her car broke down and it took her 3 3/4 hours to walk home. What is the distance between home and work, and how fast did she walk? (Hint: Express both times in hours and in decimal form before you begin.)

5. Joanne and Jenny both walked to the park. Joanne walked at four mph and Jenny walked at three mph. It took Joanne two hours to make the trip. How long did it take Jenny to make the trip, and how far away is the park?

6. A horse traveled 9 miles at an average speed of 15 mph. On the return trip it traveled 3 mph slower. How long did the return trip take?

Answer the questions.

1. George climbed Mt. Monadnock at 3 kilometers per hour. The trail was 10.5 kilometers long. How long did it take him to climb the mountain?

2. Later George walked around Dublin Lake at 7 km per hour. He walked for 4 hours and 15 minutes. How far did he go?

3. Inspired by his success at climbing and walking, George took up running. He jogged 10 km in 1.5 hours. How fast did he jog?

4-5. Lewis and Vaughn both drove their families to a camp that was 420 miles away. Lewis drove at 60 mph and Vaughn drove 10 mph less than Lewis. Lewis left at 8:30 a.m. and arrived at 3:30 p.m. Vaughn left at 8:00 a.m. How long did the trip take, and when did Vaughn arrive?

6-7. On the return trip, they decided to try a longer but more scenic route. Vaughn left at 8:40 a.m. and arrived home at 5:00 p.m. Lewis left at 9:30 a.m., yet arrived home at the same time as his friend. Vaughn's average speed was 6 mph less than Lewis's average speed. How long was the new way? What were the speeds of Lewis and Vaughn on the return trip?

Use unit multipliers to change the units of measure.

8. 12,500 lb = _____ tons

9. 3.4 m = _____ cm

10. 500 in^2 = _____ ft^2

11. 14,000 mm^2 = _____ m^2

Use unit multipliers to convert from imperial to metric or metric to imperial measure.

12.   4 gal = _____ liters   13.   75 cm = _____ in

For #14–16: Carbon and oxygen are present in 1,204 grams of CO.

14.   List all the possible equations.

15.   What is the mass of the oxygen?

16.   What is the mass of the carbon?

17.   Solve for F: $C = \dfrac{5}{9}(F - 32)$

For #18–19, use the atomic weight table.

18.   Find the percentage of sodium in NaCl.

19.   Find the percentage of chlorine in NaCl.

Solve.

20. $\left[(64)^{1/2}\right]^{2/3} =$

Answer the questions.

1. Ethan is in training for the triathlon. Monday he swam 500 yards in 30 minutes. If he swam 1,750 yards in all, how long was he in the water?

2. The next day, Ethan rode his bike at 12 mph for 2 hours and 15 minutes. How far did he go?

3. The third day, Ethan jogged 16 miles at 2 1/2 miles an hour. How long did he jog?

4-5. Arthur and Mbaga were riding their jet skis on Lake Victoria. Arthur's rate was 24 kph and Mbaga's rate was 20 kph. They raced their water craft in a straight line, and Arthur arrived 15 minutes sooner than Mbaga. How far did they travel? How long did the trip take?

6-7. On the way back to the pier, they decided to canoe. Mbaga paddled at 7.5 kph and Arthur paddled at 6 kph. It took Arthur an extra hour to return. How far is the return distance? How long did it take Arthur to make the return trip?

Use unit multipliers to change the units of measure.

8. 78 qt = _____ gal

9. 105,600 oz = _____ tons

10. 7 yd^2 = _____ ft^2

11. 100 km^2 = _____ m^2

Use unit multipliers to convert from imperial to metric or metric to imperial measure.

12.   23 m = _____ in

13.   15 m = _____ yd

For #14–16: The diligent student noticed that the ratio of homework days to non-homework days was two to one. If there are 32 days of no homework, on how many days does the student have homework?

14.   List all the possible ratios.

15.   Which one will be used and why?

16.   Solve to find how many days the student has homework.

17.   Solve for X: $\dfrac{1}{X} = \dfrac{2}{Y} + \dfrac{3}{Z}$

For #18–19, use the atomic weight table.

18.   Find the percentage of potassium in KCN.

19.   Find the percentage of nitrogen in KCN.

Solve.

20. $(i^2)(i^3) =$

Answer the questions.

1. Mark made a go-cart for Caitlyn. On her first ride, she went 15 yards per minute for 180 yards. How long did that ride take?

2. The second ride was better. Caitlyn rode for 15 minutes at 18 yards per minute, or 18 ypm. How far did she go this time?

3. On the third day, Caitlyn went 525 yards in 21 minutes. How fast was she driving?

4-5. Frank and Glenda took different flights to New England. Frank left at 8:30 a.m. and Glenda left at 7:00 a.m. They both arrived at the airport at noon. Frank's jet averaged 500 mph. How far was the trip, and how fast did Glenda travel?

6-7. On the way back, Frank took a bus, and Glenda took the train. The bus averaged 50 miles per hour, including all the stops. The train, however, arrived home 10 hours before the bus and traveled 20 mph faster. What was the rate of the train, and how long did it take Frank to get home?

Use unit multipliers to change the units of measure.

8. 17 gal = _____ pt

9. 1 qt = _____ pt

10. 2 yd^3 = _____ in^3

11. 5.6 cm^3 = _____ mm^3

Use unit multipliers to convert from imperial to metric or metric to imperial measure.

12.   18 oz = _____ g

13.   17 liters = _____ qt

For #14-16:   Nitrogen and fluorine are present in 2,059 grams of NF_3.

14.   List all the possible equations.

15.   What is the mass of the nitrogen?

16.   What is the mass of the fluorine?

17.   Solve for C: $F = \dfrac{9}{5}C - 32$

For #18–19, use the atomic weight table.

18.   Find the percentage of carbon in CF_2Cl_2.

19.   Find the percentage of chlorine in CF_2Cl_2.

Follow the directions.

20.   Find the conjugate of $(7 + 5i)$.

Area problems with unknowns will produce second-degree polynomials, and volume problems will produce third-degree polynomials. This lesson will combine polynomial multiplication and geometry skills. Expand the polynomials in your answers.

Follow the directions.

1. Find the area of the figure shown on the right.
   Dimensions are in feet. All angles are right angles.

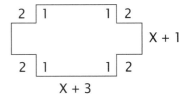

2. Find the area of #1 if X = 3 feet.

3. Find the volume of the figure shown on the right.
   All angles are right angles.

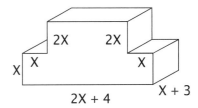

4. The volume of a sphere can be found with the formula $4/3 \, \pi \, r^3$.
   Find the volume of a sphere with a radius of X + 2.

A number like 25 is said to be a perfect square because it has a whole-number square root (in this case the square root is 5). The number 8 is a perfect cube because it has a whole-number cube root, which is 2. There are some numbers that are both perfect squares and perfect cubes.

Example 1

$8^2 = 8 \times 8 = 64$ 64 is a perfect square with a square root of 8.

$4^3 = 4 \times 4 \times 4 = 64$ 64 is a perfect cube with a cube root of 4.

You might think that numbers that are both perfect squares and perfect cubes are rare. Actually, it is easy to show that there is an infinite number of them. Look carefully at the relationships below.

Example 2

$n^6 = n^3 \times n^3 = (n^3)^2$ n^6 is a perfect square with a square root of n^3.

$n^6 = n^2 \times n^2 \times n^2 = (n^2)^3$ n^6 is a perfect cube with a cube root of n^2.

5. Find three more numbers (n^6), besides 64, that are both perfect squares and perfect cubes.

6. Using n as in example 2, write a set of equations that shows how to find numbers that are both perfect squares and have whole-number fifth roots.

Solve these motion problems. Include a sketch of each problem.

1. Two trains left the station at 8:30 a.m., traveling in opposite directions. The first train traveled at 50 mph and the second at 90 mph. What time will it be when the trains are 350 miles apart?

2. A horse trotted at 12 mph, and then walked at 5 mph for a total distance of 39 miles. If the trip took five hours, how long did the horse trot, and how long did it walk?

3. The prodigal son and his father began running toward each other when they were one mile apart. The father ran at a rate of 10 miles an hour, and the son, who was weak and tired, ran at a rate of 5 miles an hour. How long did it take them to meet?

4. Madison walked north at 3 mph. Logan left one hour later and walked south at 5 mph. If Madison started at 2:30 p.m., what time was it when they were 19 miles apart?

5. For the first part of my trip, I could average only 40 mph. Later, I was able to travel at 65 mph. If it took me seven hours to go a total of 360 miles, how long did I travel at each rate of speed?

Solve these motion problems. Include a sketch of each problem.

1. The scout left camp and crept forward at a rate of two miles an hour. Unknown to him, the enemy troops had left their camp an hour earlier and were moving toward him at a rate of 13 miles an hour. If the two camps were 20 miles apart, how long did the scout travel before he met the enemy?

2. After saying goodbye, Rachel and Sarah walked slowly away from each other. Rachel took 30 steps a minute and Sarah took 25 steps a minute. How long will they have walked when there are 1,320 steps between them?

3. Seth began the 500-mile race at 130 mph, and then slowed to 110 mph. If he drove three times as long at 130 mph, how long did he drive at each rate?

4. Mike left his home in California two days before Luke left his home in Massachusetts. Mike traveled at an average rate of 400 miles a day, and Luke traveled at an average rate of 500 miles a day. If their homes are 3,050 miles apart, how many days must Luke travel before they meet?

5. Mike (#4) left the place where he met Luke at 9 a.m. and traveled on east at 65 mph. Luke left three hours later and traveled west at 70 mph. At what time will they be 600 miles apart?

Answer the questions.

1. Rocky jumped rope for training. He jumped 100 times at a rate of 40 jumps per minute. How long did it take him?

2. The next day, Rocky jumped 129 times in three minutes. How fast did he jump?

3. The third day, Rocky jumped at a rate of 60 jumps per minute for 2 1/4 minutes. How may times did he jump?

4-5. The last day of the fair, a man challenged a horse in a race around the track. The horse and man both finished the race. The horse trotted around the course at 20 mph and completed the race in six minutes. It took the man 10 minutes. How fast did the man run, and how long is the track?

6-8. Arnold bought walkie-talkies for his parents for their anniversary. They tried them out right away to test their range. They walked in opposite directions until they were 4,000 yards apart. Amos left immediately, walking at 240 yards per minute. Eunice left two minutes later, walking at 200 yards per minute. Draw a picture of the problem and tell how long Eunice walked, how long Amos walked, and how far they each walked.

9-11. Two dogs were at the trash can when the firecracker exploded. They took off in opposite directions. When they were 600 feet apart, they halted. Emmett had traveled 27 feet per second for 10 seconds. Princess had traveled faster and longer by one second. How fast was Princess, and how far did they each run?

Use unit multipliers to change the units of measure.

12. 100 in = _____ yd

13. 4,320 in^3 = _____ ft^3

Use unit multipliers to convert from imperial to metric or metric to imperial measure.

14. 5 m = _____ in

15. 80 qt = _____ liters

For #16–18: Magnesium and oxygen are present in 720 grams of MgO.

16. List all the possible equations.

17. What is the mass of the oxygen?

18. What is the mass of the magnesium?

Follow the directions.

19. Simplify using fractional exponents. $\sqrt{\sqrt[3]{x}}$

20. Simplify. $3\sqrt{-18} - 5\sqrt{-8}$

Answer the questions.

1. Marilyn typed for seven minutes at 30 words per minute. How many words did she type?

2. Later that morning Marilyn typed 385 words in 11 minutes. How fast did she type?

3. When Marilyn was warmed up that afternoon, she typed 820 words at 40 wpm. How long did it take her?

4-5. Two aspiring marathon runners completed their running on the same regulation track. Bill ran 4 1/2 hours at 6 mph. If Kip finished in four hours, what was his rate? How long was the track?

6-8. Dan left Atlanta heading for Tampa. Chris left Tampa headed for Atlanta, 400 miles away. Dan left at 7:00 a.m. but traveled 5 mph slower than Chris. Chris traveled at 60 mph and left at 8:00 a.m. How long did each one travel? When did they meet?

9-11.   Sue and Carolyn were dying to see each other, even though they were 1,031 miles apart. On a whim, Sue left South Bend headed east at 5:30 a.m. Two hours later, Carolyn left Boston headed west at 51 mph. Sue traveled one mile per hour faster than Carolyn. How long did each person drive? When did they meet?

Use unit multipliers to change the units of measure.

12.   8,200 mm = _____ m

13.   790 m^2 = _____ km^2

Use unit multipliers to convert from imperial to metric or metric to imperial measure.

14.   4 km = _____ ft

15.   20 in = _____ cm

For #16–18: Steve Nye kept track of his tire sales. The ratio of white walls to black walls was six to five. If 253 tires were sold, how many had black walls?

16.   List all the possible ratios.

17.   Tell which one will be used, and why.

18.   Solve to find the number of tires with black walls.

Follow the directions.

19.   Simplify (put into standard form): $\dfrac{3i}{8 + 5i}$

20.   Expand: $(X + 10)^3$.

Answer the questions.

1. Major Eugene Brown kept in shape over the summer by doing pushups. In the beginning of the summer, he did 50 pushups in one-half minute. What was his rate per minute?

2. In midsummer, Major Brown did 20 pushups in one-third minute. What was his rate per minute?

3. By the end of summer, Major Brown did 35 pushups at a rate of 70 per minute. How long did it take him?

4-5. Driving to work, Jeff found the roads clear. That afternoon, the roads were covered with snow and ice. During morning rush hour he made it to work in 2 hours and 45 min. On the way home, he averaged 15 mph less than in the morning, and it took him 4 hours. How far is it to work, and what was his average speed coming home?

6-8. On the first leg of the 1,600-mile trip, Gerry drove by himself. For the second part of the trip, another driver helped. With several breaks, Gerry averaged 40 mph on the first leg. On the second leg, with two drivers, they averaged 20 mph more, and they drove for three more hours than on the first part of the trip. How may hours did Gerry drive on the first day? How many hours did the team drive on the second day? What was the team's rate on the second day?

9-11. On a walk-a-thon to raise money for Hosanna Home, John found he could run for some of the trek. He walked for 3 hours at 4 mph. He then ran 2 mph faster than he walked for the rest of the trek. If the walk-a-thon was for 20 miles, how long and how fast did John run?

Use unit multipliers to change the units of measure.

12. 9 yd = _____ ft

13. 35 m^2 = _____ cm^2

Use unit multipliers to convert from imperial to metric or metric to imperial measure.

14. 300 g = _____ oz

15. 16 mi = _____ km

For #16-18: Nitrogen and hydrogen are present in 646 grams of NH_3.

16. List all the possible equations.

17. What is the mass of the nitrogen?

18. What is the mass of the hydrogen?

Follow the directions.

19. Tell how many terms in the expression $(X - 3)^4$ and then expand it.

20. What is the third term of $(2X + 5)^5$?

The flow of electricity through the wires in your home may seem quite different from the movement of gears, but similar ratios can be used to describe it.

Think of the movement of electricity through a wire as being similar to the flow of water through a hose. Voltage is measured with volts. It is like the water pressure in the hose. Electricity is sent through long-distance power lines at high voltage. This is something like putting your finger partially over the end of a hose to make the water shoot out farther. Once the electric current reaches its destination, a step-down transformer reduces the voltage to a useful level.

In a step-down transformer, the electricity enters through a coil of wires with a large number of turns and leaves through a coil with a smaller number of turns. This reduces the number of volts, or amount of "pressure."

The formula looks like this: $\dfrac{N_p}{N_s} = \dfrac{E_p}{E_s}$

N_p is the number of turns in the primary coil, and N_s is the number of turns in the secondary coil. E_p represents the number of volts coming in to the primary coil, and E_s is the number of volts coming out of the secondary coil.

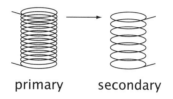

primary   secondary

Answer the questions.

1. A primary coil has 100 turns and a secondary coil has 20 turns. If 600 volts are coming into the transformer, what is the voltage of the current coming out of the transformer?

2. The number of volts coming into a transformer is 7,200, but only 240 volts are needed. If the primary coil has 480 turns, how many turns should the secondary coil have?

3. A primary coil has 500 turns and the secondary coil has 300 turns. If the output is 750 volts, how many volts are coming into the transformer?

Follow the directions.

1. Estimate the slope.

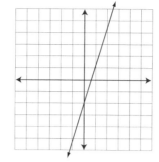

2. Estimate the intercept.

3. Estimate the slope.

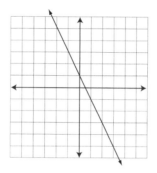

4. Estimate the intercept.

5. Write 3X + 2Y = 9 in the slope-intercept form.

6. Write Y = 5X + 1 in the standard form of the equation of a line.

7. Write 2X + 1/2Y = 3 in the slope-intercept form.

8. Write Y = X + 8 in the standard form of the equation of a line.

Given the following points, find the slope of the line by using the formula.

9. (2, 1) and (–3, –4)

10. (–3, 2) and (5, 1)

11. (1, –6) and (5, 2)

12. (–1, 4) and (1, –2)

Given the following information, find the slope if necessary, find the intercept, write both forms of the equation, and graph the line.

13. slope of 2 through the point (–2, –5)

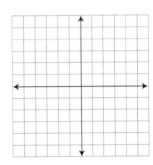

14. two points: (–2, 2) and (3, –4)

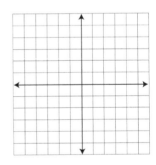

15. slope of –1 through the point (5, 5)

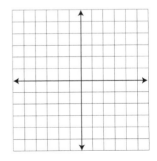

Follow the directions.

1. Estimate the slope.

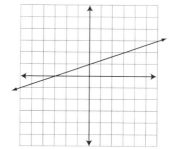

2. Estimate the intercept.

3. Estimate the slope.

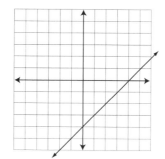

4. Estimate the intercept.

5. Write X + 7Y = 14 in the slope-intercept form.

6. Write Y = 2/3 X + 6 in the standard form of the equation of a line.

7. Write 1/3 X + 2Y = 2 in the slope-intercept form.

8. Write Y = 5X – 4 in the standard form of the equation of a line.

Given the following points, find the slope of the line by using the formula.

9. (6, 4) and (–2, –3)

10. (–2, 1) and (6, 5)

11. (2, –3) and (1, 8)

12. (–5, 3) and (1, –4)

Given the following information, find the slope if necessary, find the intercept, write both forms of the equation, and graph the line.

13. two points: (3, –6) and (0, 0)

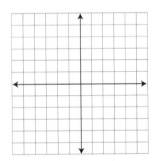

14. slope is –5, through the point (2, 6)

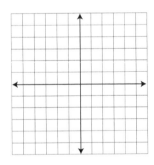

15. two points: (–4, 0) and (1, 5)

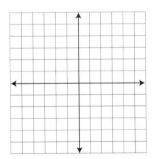

Follow the directions.

1. Estimate the slope m.

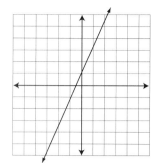

2. Estimate the intercept b.

Given the slope 1/2 through the point $(6, 2)$:

3. Find the intercept.

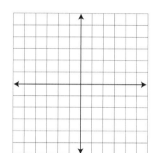

4. Write the slope/intercept formula.

5. Write the standard equation of a line.

6. Graph the line.

Given the two points $(5, -1)$ and $(1, 5)$:

7. Find the slope and intercept.

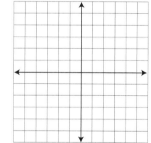

8. Write the slope/intercept formula.

9. Write the standard equation of a line.

10. Graph the line.

11-13. Chelsea and Miranda were swinging when a skunk sprayed the area. They ran in opposite directions for 15 seconds, and then stopped 360 feet apart. Miranda ran 2 feet per second slower than Chelsea. How fast and how far did they each run?

14-15. Gina walked and ran one morning. She walked four times as long as she ran. She went 14 miles and ran 3 mph faster than she walked. If she walked 5 mph, how long did she walk, how long did she run, and how far did she travel doing each?

Use unit multipliers to change the units.

16. $5,000 \text{ ft}^3 = \_\_\_\_\_ \text{ in}^3$

Use unit multipliers to convert from imperial to metric measure.

17.   100 oz = _____ g

For #18–20: A compound is CHF_3.

18.   What percent of the compound is carbon?

19.   What percent of the compound is hydrogen?

20.   What percent of the compound is fluorine?

Follow the directions.

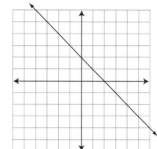

1. Estimate the slope m.

2. Estimate the intercept b.

Given the slope −4/3 through the point (3, 2):

3. Find the intercept.

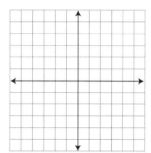

4. Write the slope/intercept formula.

5. Write the standard equation of a line.

6. Graph the line.

Given the two points (1, 2) and (−3, 4):

7. Find the slope and intercept.

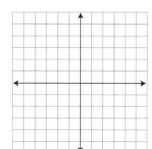

8. Write the slope/intercept formula.

9. Write the standard equation of a line.

10. Graph the line.

11-13. At 6:00 p.m., Chuck got tired of waiting for Mark and began jogging towards his house at a rate of 9 mph. At 6:20 p.m., Mark left for Chuck's traveling 45 mph. They live 12 miles apart. When did they meet, and how far did they each travel?

14-15. Fred left Los Angeles headed for Baltimore 2,880 miles away. For the first 32 hours, he averaged 12 mph faster than the next 16 hours. How fast did he go on the first 32-hour leg, and how fast on the second leg? How far did he travel on each leg?

Use unit multipliers to change the unit of measure.

16. $1,300 \text{ ft}^2 = $ _____ in^2

Use unit multipliers to convert from imperial to metric measure.

17.   20 lb = _____ kg

For #18–20: There are 350 grams of CHF_3.

18.   What is the mass of the carbon?

19.   What is the mass of the hydrogen?

20.   What is the mass of the fluorine?

Follow the directions.

1. Estimate the slope m.

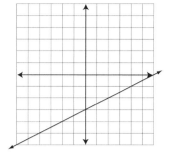

2. Estimate the intercept b.

Given the slope 5/2 through the point $(-2,-1)$:

3. Find the intercept.

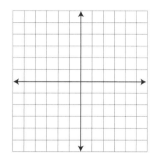

4. Write the slope/intercept formula.

5. Write the standard equation of a line.

6. Graph the line.

Given the two points $(-1, -3)$ and $(1, 5)$:

7. Find the slope and intercept.

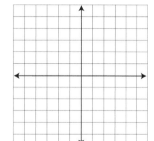

8. Write the slope/intercept formula.

9. Write the standard equation of a line.

10. Graph the line.

11-13. Romeo raced to the palace post office to get Juliet's letter. He made it in 30 minutes. On the way home he sauntered as he read. He ran 6 mph faster than he walked. It took him two hours to get home. How fast did he run and walk? How far is it to the palace post office?

14-15. Marge walked dejectedly to the mailbox at the end of the long driveway at 225 feet per minute. She ran back four times as fast as she walked. Her time walking was 3.6 minutes more than her time running. How far is it to the mailbox, and how long did it take her to run back?

Use unit multipliers to change the units.

16. $400 \text{ ft}^2 = \underline{\hspace{1cm}} \text{ yd}^2$

Use unit multipliers to convert from imperial to metric or metric to imperial measure.

17. $.75 \text{ kg} = \underline{\hspace{1cm}} \text{ lb}$

For #18–20: A compound is Na_3PO_4.

18. What percent of the compound is sodium?

19. What percent of the compound is phosphorus?

20. What percent of the compound is oxygen?

Below are a number of formulas using variables. These are all science related. You will learn more about them in your science classes, so do not be concerned if you do not understand the concepts now. Also, we are ignoring units of measure for now in order to focus on manipulating the formulas themselves.

Rearrange each formula to isolate the requested variable. Replace the letters with the data given and solve.

1. Density: $\rho = \dfrac{m}{V}$

    ρ (Greek letter rho) = density, m = mass, and V = volume

    Find the mass (m) if the density (ρ) is 10 and the volume (V) is .009.

2. Frequency: $f = \dfrac{1}{T}$

    f = frequency, T = period (a unit of time)

    Find the period (T) if the frequency (f) is 1.3.

3. Potential energy: $PE = m \cdot g \cdot h$

    PE = potential energy, m = mass, g = acceleration due to gravity, h = height

    Find the height (h) needed for a potential energy (PE) of 1,764 if the mass (m) is 30, and the acceleration due to gravity (g) is 9.8.

4. Coulomb's Law: $F = \dfrac{k \cdot q_1 \cdot q_2}{r^2}$

F = magnitude of force, q_1 = charge of one object,
q_2 = charge of second object, r = distance between the objects,
k (constant) = 9.0×10^9

Find the distance between the objects if
$q_1 = 4.0 \times 10^{-2}$, $q_2 = 2.0 \times 10^{-3}$, and $F = 1.8 \times 10^5$.

In this case, isolate r^2 and solve for it, and then find the square root.

5. Ideal gas law: PV = nRT

P = pressure, V = volume, n = number of moles (related to the number of molecules),
R (constant) = 0.0821, T = temperature in degrees Kelvin

Find the volume of .5 moles (n) of a gas at .95 units of pressure (P) and 293° K (T).

Fill in the blank.

1. Two lines that are parallel have the _____ slope and _____ intercepts.

2. If two lines are perpendicular, the slope of one is the _____ _____ of the other.

Follow the directions.

3. Find the slope and intercept of the line that is parallel to Y = 3X + 2 while passing through the point (0, 0).

4. Describe the new line in slope/intercept form.

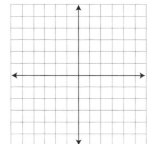

5. Graph both lines.

6. Find the slope and intercept of the line that is parallel to Y = 2X −1 while passing through the point (3, 1).

7. Describe the new line in slope/intercept form.

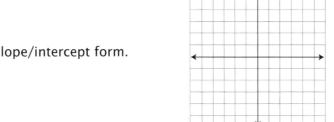

8. Graph both lines.

9. Find the slope and intercept of the line that is perpendicular to Y = –X + 4 while passing through the point (–1, 5).

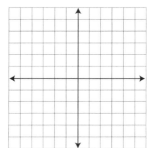

10. Describe the new line in slope/intercept form.

11. Graph both lines.

12. Graph the inequality Y ≤ X + 3.

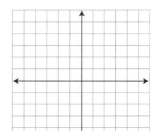

13. Graph the inequality –Y > 2X + 1.

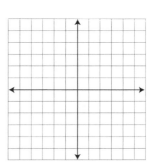

Fill in the blank.

1. Two lines that are _____ have the same slope and different intercepts.

2. If two lines are _____, the slope of one is the negative reciprocal of the other.

Follow the directions.

3. Find the slope and intercept of the line that is perpendicular to Y = 1/2 X – 3 while passing through the point (4, –1).

4. Describe the new line in slope/intercept form.

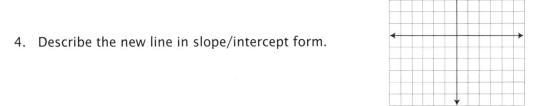

5. Graph both lines.

6. Find the slope and intercept of the line that is perpendicular to Y = –3X while passing through the point (–1, 3).

7. Describe the new line in slope/intercept form.

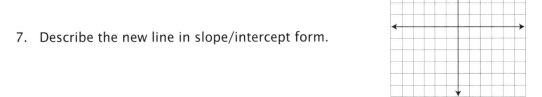

8. Graph both lines.

9. Find the slope and intercept of the line that is parallel to 3Y = X + 12 while passing through the point (−2, −2).

10. Describe the new line in slope/intercept form.

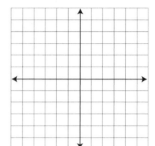

11. Graph both lines.

12. Graph the inequality 5Y > 10X + 20.

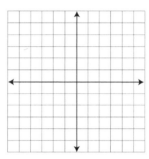

13. Graph the inequality −2Y ≥ 8X + 4.

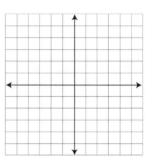

Follow the directions.

1. Find the slope and intercept of the line that is parallel to to Y = X – 3 while passing through the point (1, 0).

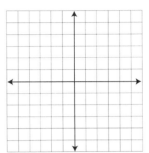

2. Write the slope/intercept formula of the new line.

3. Write the equation of the new line in standard form.

4. Graph the new line.

For #5-8: Graph 2Y > –3X + 4.

5. Graph 2Y = –3X + 4.

6. Plot two points, one on each side of the line.

7. Put the points in the equation, and test whether they are true or not.

8. Shade in the graph and make the line solid or dotted.

Given the two points (2, 3) and (0, 0):

9. Find the slope and intercept.

10. Write the slope/intercept formula.

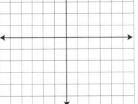

11. Write the standard equation of the line.

12. Graph the line.

13-15. Ethan was in the market for a new car. He decided to buy one from his Grampy. They were to meet on the turnpike. They live 260 miles apart. Ethan left first and Grampy left one hour later. They drove at the same speed. The total time for the trip is five hours. How far did they each drive? What was their speed?

Use unit multipliers to change the units.

16. $3 \text{ mi}^2 = $ _____ yd^2

Use unit multipliers to convert from imperial to metric measure.

17. 88 gal = _____ liters

For #18-20: A compound is $MgCrO_4$.

18. What percent of the compound is magnesium?

19. What percent of the compound is chromium?

20. What percent of the compound is oxygen?

Follow the directions.

1. Find the slope and intercept of the line that is perpendicular to 2Y = −6X + 10 while passing through the point (−1, 0).

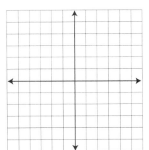

2. Write the slope/intercept formula of the new line.

3. Write the equation of the new line in standard form.

4. Graph the new line.

For #5–8: Graph Y < 3X + 1.

5. Graph Y = 3X + 1.

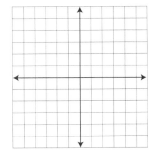

6. Plot two points, one on each side of the line.

7. Put the points in the equation, and test whether they are true or not.

8. Shade in the graph, and make the line solid or dotted.

Given the two points (−3, −2) and (5, 2):

9. Find the slope and intercept.

10. Write the slope/intercept formula.

11. Write the standard equation of the line.

12. Graph the line.

13-15. Julius rode his chariot for five hours and jogged for two-thirds of an hour. His chariot goes three times as fast as he can jog. If he went 94 miles, what was the speed of his chariot and the rate of his jogging?

Use unit multipliers to change the units.

16. $14{,}500 \text{ in}^3 =$ _____ ft^3

Use unit multipliers to convert from imperial to metric measure.

17. $50 \text{ oz} =$ _____ kg

For #18-20: There are 1,260 grams of the compound $MgCrO_4$.

18.   How many grams are magnesium?

19.   How many grams are chromium?

20.   How many grams are oxygen?

Follow the directions.

1. Find the slope and intercept of the line that is parallel to to 2Y = X while passing through the point (–2, –3).

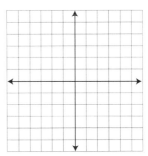

2. Write the slope/intercept formula of the new line.

3. Write the equation of the new line in standard form.

4. Graph the new line.

For #5–8: Graph –Y ≥ 2X.

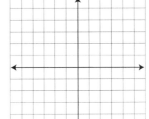

5. Graph –Y = 2X.

6. Plot two points, one on each side of the line.

7. Put the points in the equation, and test whether they are true or not.

8. Shade in the graph, and make the line solid or dotted.

Given the two points (−1, −3) and (4, 4):

9. Find the slope and the intercept.

10. Write the slope/intercept formula.

11. Write the standard equation of the line.

12. Graph the line.

13-15. The prodigal son was 60 miles from home when he left the pig slop. He started walking toward home at 4 mph. His father saw him coming and ran to meet him at 8 mph. If the son walked 12 hours before they met, how long did the father run?

Use unit multipliers to change the units.

16. $7.6 \text{ m}^3 = $ _____ cm^3

Use unit multipliers to convert from metric to imperial measure.

17.   620 km = _____ mi

For #18–20: A compound is C_2H_5Cl.

18.   What percent of the compound is carbon?

19.   What percent of the compound is hydrogen?

20.   What percent of the compound is chlorine?

21H

You will be learning how to graph several kinds of equations in your text. Another kind of graph is produced when the exponent is an unknown. These graphs show what happens when an amount increases exponentially.

Follow the directions to make a graph of an exponential increase.

1. A scientist starts with 1,000 bacteria in a dish. The number of bacteria doubles every 2 hours. Fill in the missing values to make a chart of the first 16 hours of bacterial growth.

t (hours)	0	2	4	6	8	10	12	14	16
b (bacteria in thousands)	1	2	4						

Notice that each value of *b* can be written as 2 with an exponent.

2. Plot the points from the chart on the graph below and connect them with a curved line showing the growth in numbers of bacteria. (Estimate the location of the value of *b* for each point.)

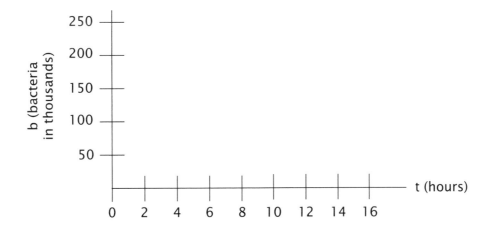

3. The exponential growth of a system is represented by $Y = 2^X + 4$.
   Find the value of Y for each value of X on the chart at right.

X	Y
0	
1	
2	
3	
-1	
-2	
-3	

4. Plot the values from #3 on the graph below, estimating as necessary.

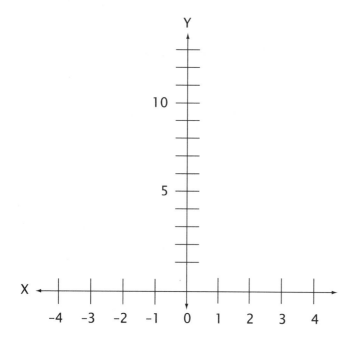

5. As X values increase, what do you notice about the rate of increase over time indicated by the Y value?

Follow the directions.

1. Write the distance formula.

2. Write the midpoint formula.

3. Plot these points: A (–2, 3), B (1, 5), C (3, –2), D (–1, –1), E (–4, –3).

4. Compute the distance between A and B.

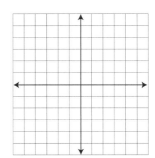

5. Compute the distance between B and C.

6. Compute the distance between D and E.

7. Plot these points: A (–4, 4), B (3, 2), C (5, –3), D (2, –3), E (–5, –2).

8. Compute the distance between A and B.

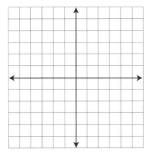

9. Compute the distance between B and C.

10. Compute the distance between D and E.

11. Plot these points: A (–6, 2), B (–2, 4), C (3, 4), D (4, –3), E (–2, –2).

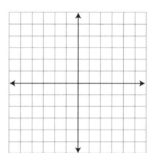

12. Find the midpoint between points A and D.

13. Find the midpoint between points B and D.

14. Find the midpoint between points E and C.

15. Plot these points: A (0, 0), B (–3, 5), C (5, 1), D (0, –3), E (–4, –1).

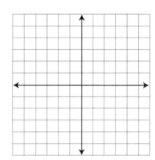

16. Find the midpoint between points A and C.

17. Find the midpoint between points B and E.

18. Find the midpoint between points A and D.

Follow the directions.

1. Write the distance formula.

2. Write the midpoint formula.

3. Plot these points: A (–1, 5), B (2, 2), C (5, 3), D (1, 1), E (–6, –6).

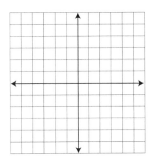

4. Compute the distance between A and B.

5. Compute the distance between B and C.

6. Compute the distance between D and E.

7. Plot these points: A (–2, 3), B (5, 1), C (3, –2), D (–1, –1), E (–3, –4).

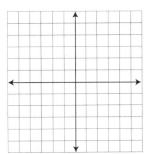

8. Compute the distance between A and B.

9. Compute the distance between B and C.

10. Compute the distance between D and E.

11. Plot these points: A (–3, 5), B (2, 6), C (4, –4), D (–2, –5), E (–5, –3).

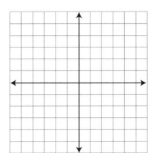

12. Find the midpoint between points A and D.

13. Find the midpoint between points B and D.

14. Find the midpoint between points E and C.

15. Plot these points: A (–2, –2), B (1, 1), C (2, –1), D (4, –2), E (2, –6).

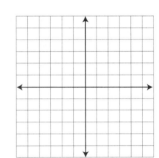

16. Find the midpoint between points A and B.

17. Find the midpoint between points C and D.

18. Find the midpoint between points D and E.

Given points A (−1, −2), B (−3, 4), C (−1, 6), D (3, 5), and E (4, 1):

1. Plot points A, B, C, D, and E.

2. Draw a line between A and E.

3. Make a right triangle.

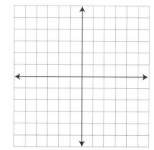

4. Find the length of the legs.

5. Use the Pythagorean theorem to find the distance between points A and E.

6. Compute the distance between points A and B.

7. Compute the distance between points B and C.

8. Compute the distance between points C and E.

9. Find the midpoint between points B and E.

10. Find the midpoint between points B and D.

11. Find the midpoint between points A and C.

Given points (4, 3) and (−5, −1):

12. Find the slope/intercept formula of the line.

13. Graph the line.

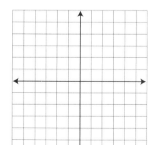

Given line Y = 3X – 1/2:

14. Find the slope/intercept formula of the line parallel to the given line through the point (2, –2).

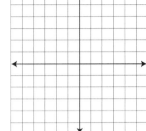

15. Graph the line.

Given line Y = –2/5 X + 1/3:

16. Find the slope/intercept formula of the line perpendicular to the given line through the point (–3, –3).

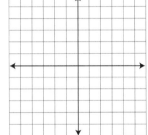

17. Graph the line.

Given Y ≤ –2X – 4:

18. Graph the line.

19. Plot two points and test them.

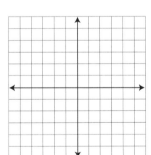

20. Shade the graph, and make the line dotted or solid.

Given points A (–6, 6), B (0, 5), C (4, 3), D (0, 0), and E (–5, –2):

1. Plot points A, B, C, D, and E.

2. Draw a line between C and D.

3. Make a right triangle.

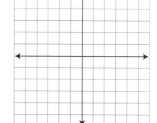

4. Find the length of the legs.

5. Use the Pythagorean theorem to find the distance between points C and D.

6. Compute the distance between points A and D.

7. Compute the distance between points C and E.

8. Compute the distance between points B and D.

9. Find the midpoint between points A and B.

10. Find the midpoint between points B and E.

11. Find the midpoint between points C and D.

Given the points (–4, 3) and (1, –3):

12. Find the slope/intercept formula of the line.

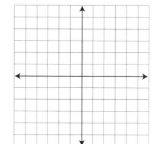

13. Graph the line.

Given line: Y = 2/3 X − 1/3:

14. Find the slope/intercept formula of the line parallel to the given line through the point (3, 4).

15. Graph the line.

Given line Y = −4X − 1:

16. Find the slope/intercept formula of the line perpendicular to the given line through the point (−2, 3).

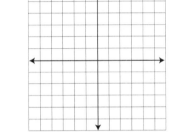

17. Graph the line.

Given 5Y ≥ 3X − 15:

18. Graph the line.

19. Plot two points and test them.

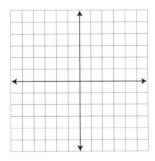

20. Shade the graph, and make the line dotted or solid.

Given points A (1, –1), B (5, –3), C (2, –6), D (–4, –2), and E (–3, 4):

1. Plot points A, B, C, D, and E.

2. Draw a line between A and E.

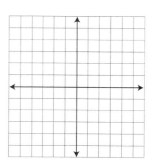

3. Make a right triangle.

4. Find the length of the legs.

5. Use the Pythagorean theorem to find the distance between points A and E.

6. Compute the distance between points B and D.

7. Compute the distance between points B and C.

8. Compute the distance between points C and E.

9. Find the midpoint between points C and D.

10. Find the midpoint between points B and E.

11. Find the midpoint between points C and E.

Given the points (4, 1) and (–1, –2):

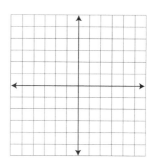

12. Find the slope/intercept formula of the line.

13. Graph the line.

Given the line $Y = 3/4\,X + 2$:

14. Find the slope/intercept formula of the line parallel to the given line through the point (1, –3).

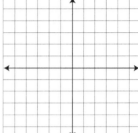

15. Graph the line.

Given the line $Y = -1/2\,X + 1$:

16. Find the slope/intercept formula of the line perpendicular to the given line through the point (0, 3).

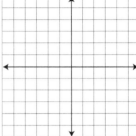

17. Graph the line.

Given $-4Y < 3X + 2$:

18. Graph the line.

19. Plot two points and test them.

20. Shade the graph, and make the line dotted or solid.

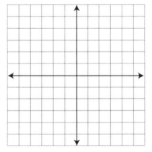

The exponent in an exponential equation can also have a negative value.

Follow the directions.

1. The exponential growth of a system is represented by $Y = 2^{-X} - 3$.
   Find the value of Y for each value of X on the chart at right.

X	Y
0	
1	
2	
3	
−1	
−2	
−3	

2. Plot the values from #1 on the graph below, estimating as necessary.

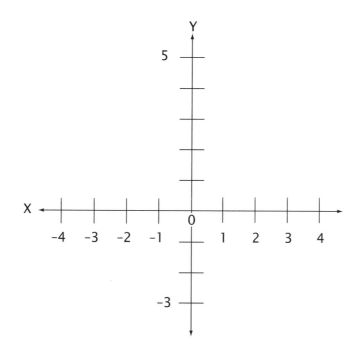

The number of students studying math is increasing according to the following equation:

$$M = A\,(1.1)^{t/d}$$

M = the number of students
A = the beginning population
d = time in which the number of students increases by 1.1
t = elapsed time in years

When doing this kind of problem, be sure that you use the same units of time for *d* and *t*.

Use the growth equation to answer the questions.

3. If A = 100 and d = 2, how many students will be studying math at the end of four years?

4. Using the information in #3, make a graph showing the relationship between *t* and *M* for values of t ≤ 10. You may use only the even values of *t* and estimate those that come between by sketching the graph. When interpreting the graph, remember that in real life students come in whole numbers!

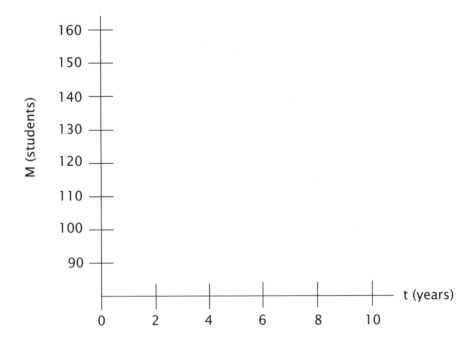

5. How many years before the number of students studying math reaches 133?

Follow the directions.

1. Given $X^2 + Y^2 = 36$, find the coordinates of the center and the radius of the circle.

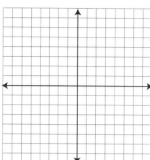

2. Graph the result of #1.

3. Given the center $(3, -3)$ and the radius (4), create the equation of the circle.

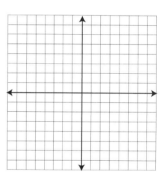

4. Graph the result of #3.

5. Given $X^2 + 2X + Y^2 + 4Y = 4$, find the center and the radius by completing the square.

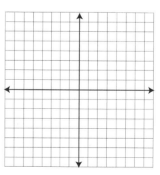

6. Graph the result of #5.

7. Given $4X^2 + Y^2 = 36$, find the coordinates of the center and the X and Y extremities.

8. Graph the result of #7.

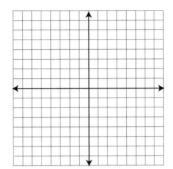

9. Given $16(X + 1)^2 + 9(Y - 1)^2 = 144$, find the coordinates of the center and the X and Y extremities.

10. Graph the result of #9.

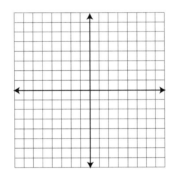

Follow the directions.

1. Given $(X + 4)^2 + (Y + 4)^2 = 5$, find the coordinates of the center and the radius of the circle.

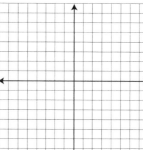

2. Graph the result of #2.

3. Given the center (2, 1) and the radius (4.5), create the equation of the circle.

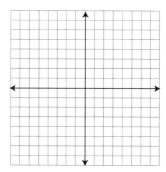

4. Graph the result of #3.

5. Given $X^2 - 8X + Y^2 + 12Y = -48$, find the center and the radius by completing the square.

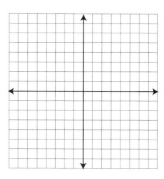

6. Graph the result of #5.

7. Given $4(X - 2)^2 + 16(Y + 1)^2 = 64$, find the coordinates of the center and the X and Y extremities.

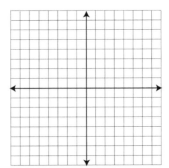

8. Graph the result of #7.

9. Given $\dfrac{(X - 1)^2}{9} + \dfrac{(Y + 1)^2}{1} = 1$, find the coordinates of the center and the X and Y extremities.

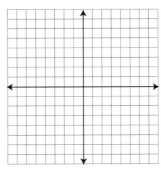

10. Graph the result of #9.

Follow the directions.

1. Given $X^2 + Y^2 = 9$, find the coordinates of the center and the radius of the circle.

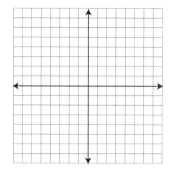

2. Graph the result of #1.

3. Given the center (1, 1) and radius (3), create the equation of the circle.

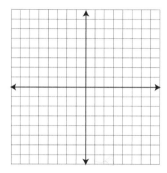

4. Graph the result of #3.

5. Given $X^2 + 6X + Y^2 + 6Y = -2$, find the center and radius by completing the square.

6. Sketch the result of #5.

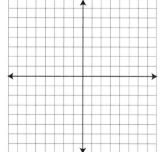

Given $6X^2 + 4Y^2 = 24$:

7. Find the coordinates of the center.

8. Find the coordinates of the X extremity.

9. Find the coordinates of the Y extremity.

10. Sketch the result.

Given points A (5, –6), B (2, 3), and C (–2, –4):

11.   Compute the distance between points B and C.

12.   Compute the distance between points A and B.

13.   Find the midpoint between points B and C.

14.   Find the midpoint between points A and C.

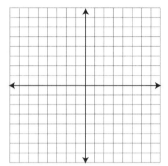

Given line 3Y = X – 6:

15.   Find the slope/intercept formula of the line parallel
      to the given line through the point (-3, 4).

16.   Graph the line.

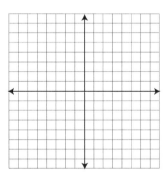

Given line 5Y = –X – 5:

17.   Find the slope/intercept formula of the line perpendicular
      to the given line through the point (-1, -3).

18.   Graph the line.

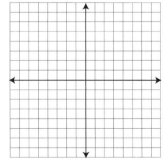

Given 2Y – 2X ≥ 3:

19.   Graph the line. Plot two points and test them.

20.   Shade the graph, and make the line dotted or solid.

Follow the directions.

1. Given $(X - 2)^2 + (Y + 3)^2 = 36$, find the coordinates of the center and the radius of the circle.

2. Graph the result of #1.

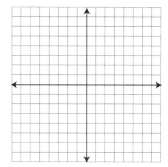

3. Given the center (–2, 0) and radius (5), create the equation of the circle.

4. Graph the result of #3.

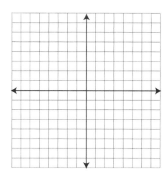

5. Given $X^2 - 6X + Y^2 = 16$, find the center and the radius by completing the square.

6. Sketch the result of #5.

Given $\dfrac{(X+3)^2}{4} + \dfrac{(Y-1)^2}{16} = 1$:

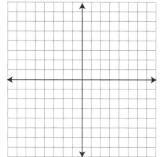

7. Find the coordinates of the center.

8. Find the coordinates of the X extremity.

9. Find the coordinates of the Y extremity.

10. Sketch the result.

Given points A (6, 1), B (−2, −1), and C (−4, 4):

11. Compute the distance between points A and B.

12. Compute the distance between points A and C.

13. Find the midpoint between points B and C.

14. Find the midpoint between points A and C.

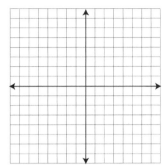

Given line 4Y + X = −2:

15. Find the slope/intercept formula of the line parallel to the given line through the point (0, −4).

16. Graph the line.

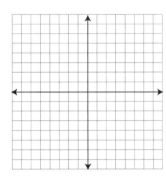

Given this line: 2Y = X + 5

17. Find the slope/intercept formula of the line perpendicular to the given line through the point (2, 3).

18. Graph the line.

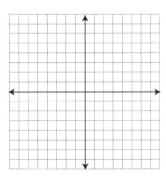

Given 5Y < 2X + 5/2:

19. Graph the line. Plot two points and test them.

20. Shade the graph and make the line dotted or solid.

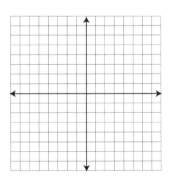

Follow the directions.

1. Given $3X^2 + 3Y^2 = 75$, find the coordinates of the center and the radius of the circle.

2. Graph the result of #1.

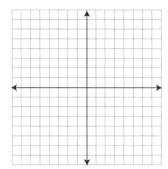

3. Given the center (2, –2) and radius (2), create the equation of the circle.

4. Graph the result of #3.

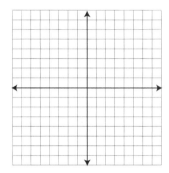

5. Given $X^2 + 2X + Y^2 + 2Y = 34$, find the center and radius of the equation by completing the square.

6. Sketch the result of #5.

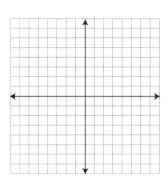

Given $\dfrac{X^2}{25} + \dfrac{Y^2}{9} = 1$:

7. Find the coordinates of the center.

8. Find the coordinates of the X extremity.

9. Find the coordinates of the Y extremity.

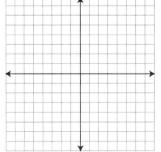

10. Sketch the result.

Given points A (3, 6), B (0, 0), and C (6, 3):

11. Compute the distance between points A and C.

12. Compute the distance between points B and C.

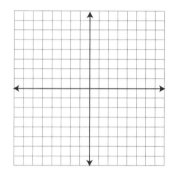

13. Find the midpoint between points A and B.

14. Find the midpoint between points A and C.

Given line $2Y + 2X = -3$:

15. Find the slope/intercept formula of the line parallel to the given line through the point (-2, 4).

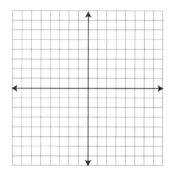

16. Graph the line.

Given this line: $Y = -3X - 2$

17. Find the slope/intercept formula of the line perpendicular to the given line through the point (1, 3).

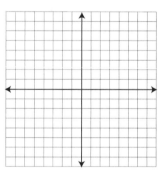

18. Graph the line.

Given $5Y + 4X \leq 0$:

19. Graph the line. Plot two points and test them.

20. Shade the graph, and make the line dotted or solid.

All the rules you have learned for solving equations work no matter what symbols are used.

Solve for X.

1. YX – YT = YZ

2. Q(X + B) = R(X + C)

3. AX – BX – C = CX + X + E

4. X(A + B + C) + Y – Z = A

5. C(X – Y) + F = CAB – CY + F

Use substitution to solve for X in the pairs of equations given.

6. $Y = R + 2X$
    $Y = S + X$

7. $Y = EX$
    $Y + EX = Q$

8. $X = Y + A$
    $X = BY - B$

9. $Y - X = Q$
    $Y + RX = T$

10. $Y - CX = C$
    $Y + DX = -D$

Estimate each graph. Plot several points to confirm your estimate, and graph the parabola.

1. $Y = 3X^2$

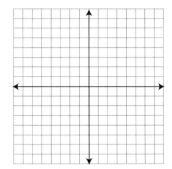

2. $Y = -X^2$

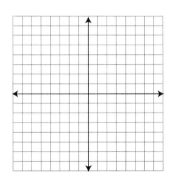

3. $Y = 1/3 \, X^2$

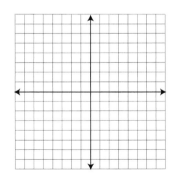

4. $X = 4Y^2$

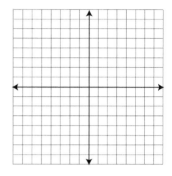

5. $X = -3Y^2 + 1$

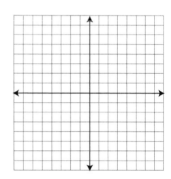

6. $Y = X^2 - 4$

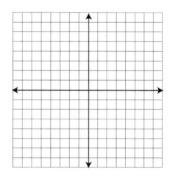

24B

Estimate each graph. Plot several points to confirm your estimate, and graph the parabola.

1. $Y = 2X^2 + 5$

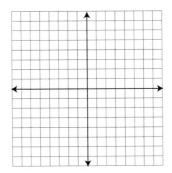

2. $2X = -4Y^2 + 8$

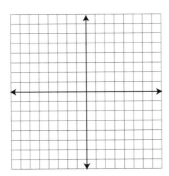

3. $X = 1/2\ Y^2 + 3$

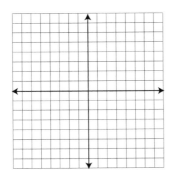

4. $3X^2 = Y + 1$

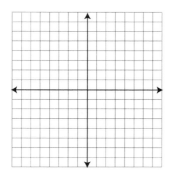

5. $Y = -6X^2 + 1/2$

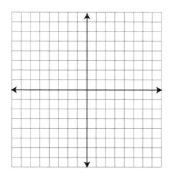

6. $X = Y^2 + 5$

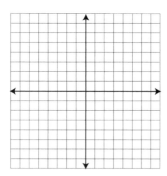

Follow the directions.

1. Estimate the graph of $Y = X^2 - 3$.

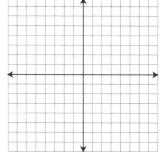

2. Plot five points to confirm your hypothesis, and graph the figure.

3. Estimate the graph of $Y = -3X^2 + 4$.

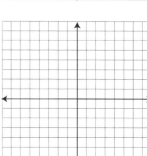

4. Plot five points to confirm your hypothesis, and graph the figure.

5. Estimate the coefficient of X^2 in parabola A.

6. Estimate the intercept of parabola A.

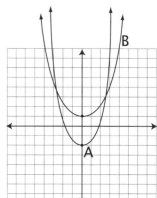

7. Estimate the coefficient of X^2 in parabola B.

8. Estimate the intercept of parabola B.

Given $2X^2 + 2Y^2 = 8$:

9. Find the center and radius of the circle.

10. Graph the result.

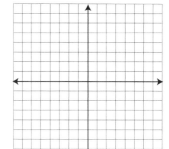

11. Given the center (1, –1) and radius (3), create the equation of the circle.

12. Graph the result.

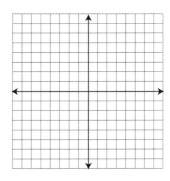

Given $\dfrac{(X)^2}{4} + \dfrac{(Y)^2}{9} = 1$:

13. Find the coordinates of the center.

14. Find the coordinates of the X and Y extremities, and sketch the result.

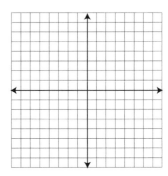

Given points A (2, –1), B (4, 4), and C (–1, 2):

15. Compute the distance between points A and B.

16. Compute the distance between points B and C.

17. Find the midpoint between points A and C.

18. Find the midpoint between points A and B.

19. Find the slope/intercept formula of the line perpendicular to 2Y + 2/3 X = 1, through the point (2, 3).

Follow the directions.

20. Graph 5Y – 3X > 5.

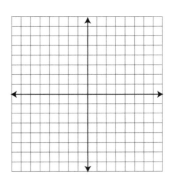

Follow the directions.

1. Estimate the graph of $2Y = X^2 + 4$.

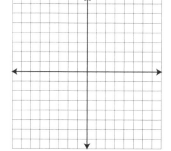

2. Plot five points to confirm your hypothesis, and graph the figure.

3. Estimate the graph of $Y = -1/2 \, X^2 - 1$.

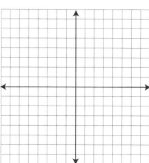

4. Plot five points to confirm your hypothesis, and graph the figure.

5. Estimate the coefficient of X^2 in parabola A.

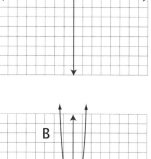

6. Estimate the intercept of parabola A.

7. Estimate the coefficient of X^2 in parabola B.

8. Estimate the intercept of parabola B.

Given $X^2 - 4X + Y^2 - 2Y = 4$:

9. Find the center and radius of the circle.

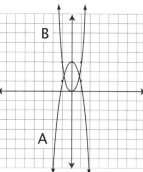

10. Graph the result.

11. Given the center (–2, –1) and radius (5), create the equation of the circle.

12. Graph the result.

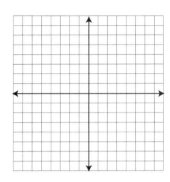

Given $(X + 2)^2 + 4(Y - 1)^2 = 16$:

13. Find the coordinates of the center.

14. Find the coordinates of the X and Y extremities, and sketch the result.

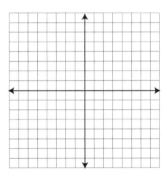

Given points A $(0, 0)$, B $(6, 3)$, and C $(-1, -3)$

15. Compute the distance between points A and B.

16. Compute the distance between points A and C.

17. Find the midpoint between points B and C.

18. Find the midpoint between points A and B.

19. Find the slope/intercept formula of the line perpendicular to 5Y = X + 10, through the point (1, –2).

Follow the directions.

20. Graph X – Y > 1/2.

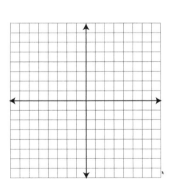

Follow the directions.

1. Estimate the graph of $2X^2 = -Y$.

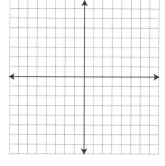

2. Plot five points to confirm your hypothesis, and graph the figure.

3. Estimate the graph of $Y + 1 = 2X^2$.

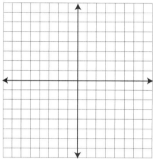

4. Plot five points to confirm your hypothesis, and graph the figure.

5. Estimate the coefficient of X^2 in parabola A.

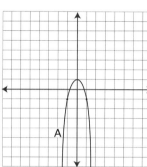

6. Estimate the intercept of parabola A.

7. Estimate the coefficient of X^2 in parabola B.

8. Estimate the intercept of parabola B.

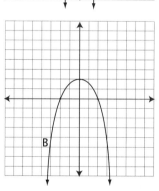

Given $1/2 \, X^2 + 1/2 \, Y^2 = 8$

9. Find the center and radius of the circle.

10. Graph the result.

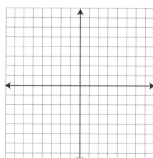

11. Given the center (0, 2) and radius (3), create the equation of the circle.

12. Graph the result.

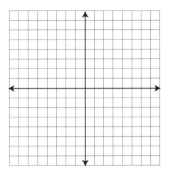

Given $\dfrac{(X-1)^2}{16} + \dfrac{(Y+1)^2}{4} = 1$:

13. Find the coordinates of the center.

14. Find the coordinates of the X and Y extremities, and sketch the result.

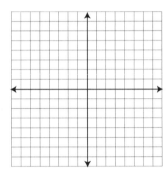

Given points A(−5, 5), B (0, 4), and C (4, −3)

15. Compute the distance between points A and B.

16. Compute the distance between points A and C.

17. Find the midpoint between points B and C.

18. Find the midpoint between points A and B.

19. Find the slope/intercept formula of the line perpendicular to 4Y − X − 6 = 0, through the point (0, 3).

Follow the directions.

20. Graph Y > 4X − 3/2.

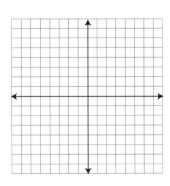

In *Algebra 1*, you used elimination to solve simultaneous equations. Once you have found the first variable, it can be substituted into one of the original equations to find the other variable.

Example 1

Solve for X in the given equations: $AX + BY = C$ $X - Y = D$

$B(X - Y) = BD$ — Multiply each side of equation 2 by B. The object is to produce a term that will be eliminated when we add the two equations.

$$\begin{aligned} AX + BY &= C \\ +BX - BY &= BD \\ \hline AX + BX &= C + BD \end{aligned}$$

Add the new equation 2 to equation 1, eliminating the Y term.

$X(A + B) = C + BD$ — Factor out X.

$X = \dfrac{C + BD}{A + B}$ — Divide both sides by (A + B).

Now solve for Y by substituting the value of X that you just found into the original equation 2.

$\dfrac{C + BD}{A + B} - Y = D$ — Substitute for X.

$-Y = D - \dfrac{C + BD}{A + B}$ — Subtract the fraction from both sides.

$Y = -D + \dfrac{C + BD}{A + B}$ — Multiply each side of the equation by (–1).

This may seem cumbersome. The point is, no matter what kinds of symbols are used in science or upper-level math courses, the rules for manipulating equations remain the same.

Eliminate Y and solve for X.

1. $AY + BX = C$ $AY + DX = -E$

Eliminate Y and solve for X. Substitute the value of X into the first equation to find the value of Y.

2. X – Y = R   AX + Y = T

Eliminate X and solve for Y in the equations below, and then answer the question.

3. Y – QX = R   Y + X = T

If R = 2, Q = 3, and T = 6, what is the value of Y?

Find the axis of symmetry and the vertex of each equation, and graph the parabola.

1. $Y = 3X^2 - 6X + 2$

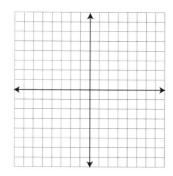

2. $4Y = 4X^2 + 8X + 4$

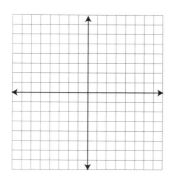

3. $Y = -X^2 + 6X - 4$

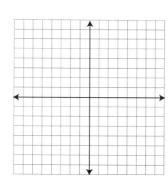

4. $Y = -4X^2 + 4X$

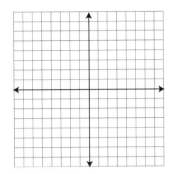

5. $Y = 1/4 \, X^2 - 3$

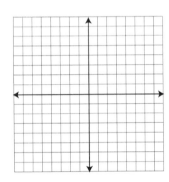

6. $Y = 3X^2 + 30X + 78$

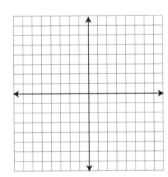

7. Alison plans to make a wall hanging. She has 36 feet of decorative edging. What is the largest rectangular hanging she can make with edging all around it?

Find the axis of symmetry and the vertex of each equation, and graph the parabola.

1. $Y = 2X^2 - 4X + 1$

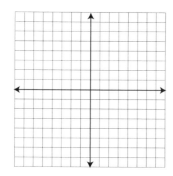

2. $Y = X^2 + X - 6$

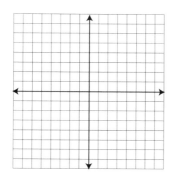

3. $5Y = -15X^2 + 30X$

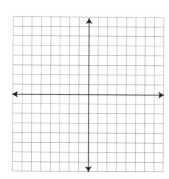

4. $Y = -2X^2 - 12X - 20$

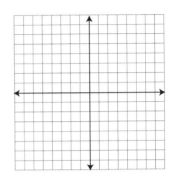

5. $Y = 1/4 X^2 + 3X + 3$

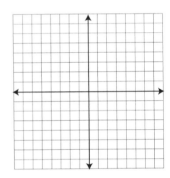

6. $X = 2Y^2 + 8Y$

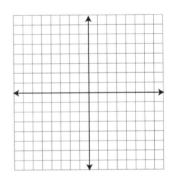

7. A gardener has enough money to build 260 feet of garden wall. He plans to use an existing wall for one side of the enclosure. What is the largest rectangular area he can enclose?

Given $6Y = 3X^2 + 24X$:

1. Find the axis of symmetry.

2. Find the vertex.

3. Sketch the graph.

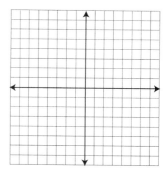

Given $Y = -2X^2 - 4X - 3$:

4. Find the axis of symmetry.

5. Find the vertex.

6. Sketch the graph.

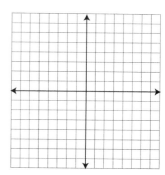

Assume $Y = AX^2 + BX + C$, and complete the statements.

7. If $A > 0$, the graph of the parabola _____.

8. C moves the graph up and down the _____.

9-10. Mike needs a fenced play area connected to the house for Alex and Megan. He has 200 ft of fencing for the rectangular space. What are the dimensions of the largest possible yard?

11. Graph $Y = 2X^2 + 2$.

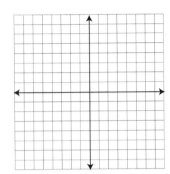

12. Graph $2Y - X^2 = -2$.

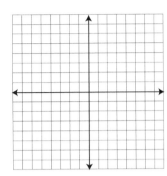

13. Find the center and the radius of $2(X - 3)^2 + 2(Y + 2)^2 = 72$.

14. Given the center (1, 4) and radius (5), create the equation of the circle.

15-16. Find the center and the radius of $X^2 + Y^2 = 4X + 5$.

Given points A (3, 5), B (−4, −1), and C (3, −2).

17. Compute the distance between points A and B.

18. Find the midpoint between points A and C.

Given $\dfrac{(X+2)^2}{16} + \dfrac{(Y+3)^2}{9} = 1$:

19. Find the center and the extremities.

20. Graph the figure.

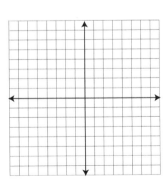

Given $Y = X^2 - 4X + 3$:

    1. Find the axis of symmetry.

    2. Find the vertex.

    3. Sketch the graph.

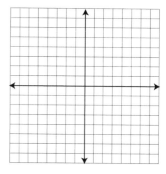

Given $2Y + X^2 = 8X - 4$:

    4. Find the axis of symmetry.

    5. Find the vertex.

    6. Sketch the graph.

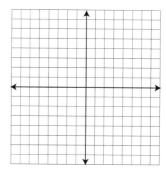

Assume $Y = AX^2 + BX + C$, and complete the statements.

    7. If $|A| > 1$, the graph is _____ than $Y = X^2$.

    8. B moves the graph _____ on the X-axis.

9-10. Ethan has a 12-foot long board. His mom needs a rectangular raised bed garden made with the board as the edge. What is the largest enclosure he can make with this board?

11. Graph $3Y + 6X^2 = 6$.

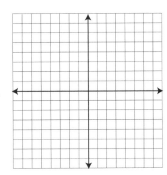

12. Graph $Y + X^2 = 0$.

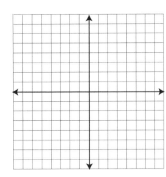

13. Find the center and the radius of $3(X + 1)^2 + 3(Y + 4)^2 = 147$.

14. Given the center $(0, -3)$ and radius (6), create the equation of the circle.

15-16. Find the center and radius of $X^2 + 4X - 3 = -Y^2 - 6Y$.

Given points A $(-2, -2)$, B $(3, -2)$, and C $(3, 2)$:

17. Compute the distance between points A and B.

18. Find the midpoint between points A and C.

Given $-3Y + 2X \leq 3$:

19. Change the equation to the slope/intercept formula.

20. Graph the figure.

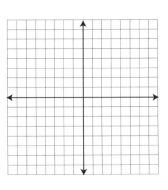

Given $Y + 2X^2 + 5 = 3X$:

1. Find the axis of symmetry.

2. Find the vertex.

3. Sketch the graph.

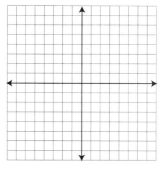

Given $Y + 2X = 3X^2 - 1$:

4. Find the axis of symmetry.

5. Find the vertex.

6. Sketch the graph.

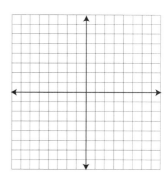

Assume $Y = AX^2 + BX + C$, and complete the statements.

7. If $A < 0$, the graph of the parabola _____.

8. The axis of symmetry is $X =$ _____.

9-10. Tara wants another fenced-in area right next to Alex's for their new puppy. If Mike uses one side from the first fence, what must the dimensions of the other three sides be in order to make 120 feet of new fencing enclose the biggest area? (Refer to 25C.)

11. Graph $4Y = -2X^2 - 8$.

12. Graph $3X^2 - Y = -1$.

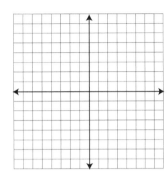

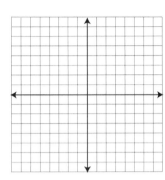

13. Find the center and the radius of $(X - 2)^2 + (Y - 3)^2 = 6^2$.

14. Given the center $(-1, -1)$ and radius (7), create the equation of the circle.

15-16. Find the center and the radius of $X^2 + Y^2 = 6Y - 5$.

Given points A $(-6, -4)$, B $(-2, -4)$, and C $(2, -6)$:

17. Compute the distance between points A and C.

18. Find the midpoint between points B and C.

Given $\dfrac{(X-1)^2}{20} + \dfrac{(Y+2)^2}{25} = 1$:

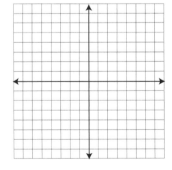

19. Find the center and the extremities.

20. Graph the figure.

Parabolas and the ideas of maxima and minima have a number of practical applications.

Tell whether the parabola represented by each equation has a maximum point or a minimum point.

1. $Y = X^2 - 3X + 1$

2. $Y = -2X^2 + 7X - 1$

3. $Y = 3X^2$

The first problem below is similar to those in your text. The others are different applications of parabola problems involving a maximum or minimum value.

Read and solve.

4. A farmer has 400 feet of fencing to build a rectangular pig pen along the side of an existing fence. What dimensions would yield the largest enclosed area?

5. The 2-Cute Shirt Company knows that its cost in dollars (C) per shirt is given by $C = .4X^2 - 2X + 5$, where X is the maximum number of groups of 1,000 shirts that should be made in order to minimize costs. Use the same formula that you used to find maximum area to find the number of groups of 1,000 shirts that should be made. How many actual shirts is that?

6. Fossil Oil Company has three million gallons of gasoline available for the Labor Day weekend. The company has determined that it can maximize its revenues by withholding some gasoline from the market. Revenue can be determined by the formula $R = 2X^2 - 60X - 36,000$, where X represents the number of 20,000-gallon batches of gasoline withheld.

   Use the maximum area formula to find the number of 20,000-gallon units of gasoline that should be withheld to maximize revenues. How many gallons of gasoline is that?

7. For every 20,000 gallons of gasoline that are withheld from the market, the remainder can be sold at a one-cent increase per gallon. The usual price for gasoline is $1.20 per gallon. Use your answer for #6 and the information given in that problem to find the price per gallon for the gasoline that is not withheld.

8. What is the actual revenue that Fossil Oil Company (#6 and 7) will receive for the gasoline that is released to the market?

For each equation, plot several points and graph.

1. XY = 8

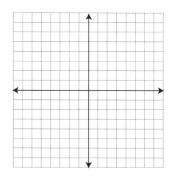

2. XY – 12 = 0

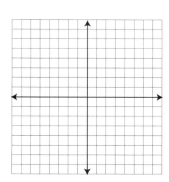

3. –XY = –5

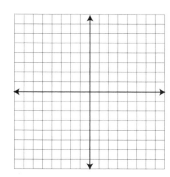

4. $X^2 - 5Y^2 = 25$

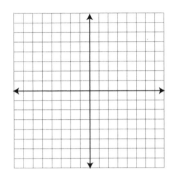

5. $3X^2 - Y^2 = 6$

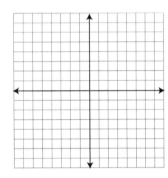

6. $5X^2 - 25 = Y^2$

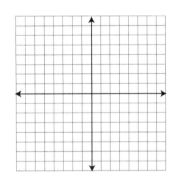

For each equation, plot several points and graph.

1. $Y = -\dfrac{3}{X}$

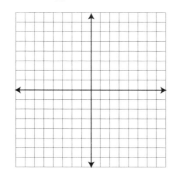

2. $0 = 4 - XY$

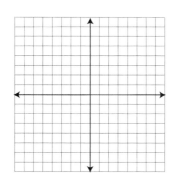

3. $-3XY = 18$

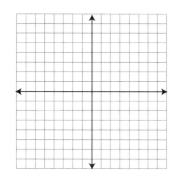

4. $1/10 \, X^2 - 1/5 \, Y^2 = 1$

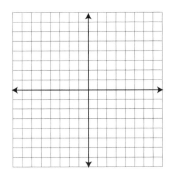

5. $2Y^2 - 3X^2 = 8$

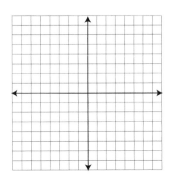

6. $Y^2 - 2X^2 = 16$

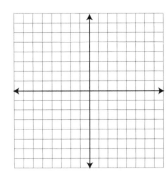

Given $XY - 4 = 0$:

   1. Plot several points.

   2. Sketch the graph.

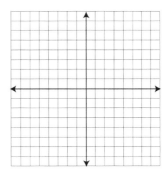

Given $Y = -6/X$:

   3. Plot several points.

   4. Sketch the graph.

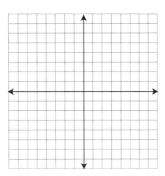

Given $2X^2 = 2Y^2 + 6$:

   5. Plot several points.

   6. Sketch the graph.

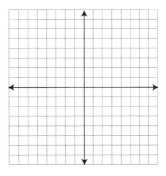

Given $Y = 2X^2 - 3X + 2$:

   7. Find the axis of symmetry.

   8. Find the vertex.

   9. Sketch the graph.

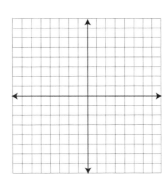

10. Graph $1/3\ Y = 2/3\ X^2 + 1/3$.

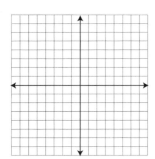

11. Graph $2Y - 6X^2 = -6$.

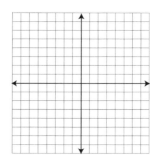

12. Find the center and the radius of $5(X - 1)^2 + 5(Y + 2)^2 = 500$.

13. Given the center (5, –2) and radius (3), create the equation of the circle.

14-15. Find the center and the radius of $9X^2 + 9Y^2 - 36X - 36Y = 252$.

Given points A (–2, 5), B (3, 1), C (–2, –2), and D (4, –4):

16. Compute the distance between points A and C.

17. Find the midpoint between points A and C.

18. What is the slope/intercept equation of the line parallel to $Y = X + 3$ through (–2, 3)?

Given $\dfrac{(X-1)^2}{9} + \dfrac{(Y+1)^2}{1} = 1$

19. Find the center and the extremities.

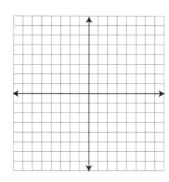

20. Graph the figure.

Given $X = -10/Y$:

   1. Plot several points.

   2. Sketch the graph.

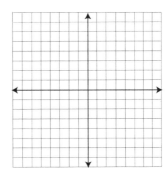

Given $Y = 8/X$:

   3. Plot several points.

   4. Sketch the graph.

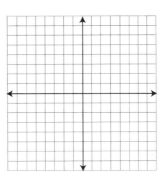

Given $-Y^2 = -X^2 + 2$:

   5. Plot several points.

   6. Sketch the graph.

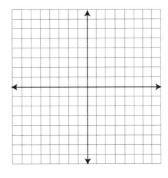

Given $Y = -3/4\,X^2 + 2X$:

   7. Find the axis of symmetry.

   8. Find the vertex.

   9. Sketch the graph.

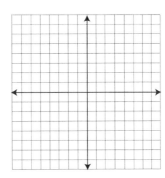

10. Graph $8X - 4Y - 4X^2 = 1$.

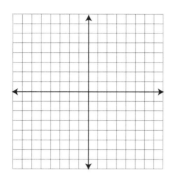

11. Graph $X^2 = -Y - 2$.

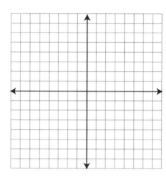

12. Find the center and the radius of $2/3 (X + 2)^2 + 2/3 (Y + 2)^2 = 54$.

13. Given the center (4, 3) and radius (8), create the equation of the circle.

14-15. Find the center and the radius of $X^2 + Y^2 - 2Y - 3 = 0$.

Given points A (−2, 5), B (3, 1), C (−2, −2), and D (4, −4):

16. Compute the distance between points B and C.

17. Find the midpoint between points B and C.

18. What is the slope/intercept equation of the line perpendicular to $2Y + 5X = 3$ through (1, 2)?

Given $4(X − 2)^2 + 16(Y + 1)^2 = 64$:

19. Find the center and the extremities.

20. Graph the figure.

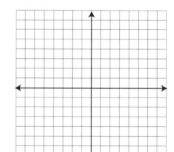

Given $XY = -12$.

   1. Plot several points.

   2. Sketch the graph.

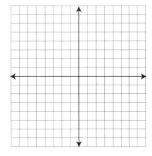

Given $-XY = -3$.

   3. Plot several points.

   4. Sketch the graph.

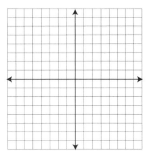

Given $9X^2 = 6Y^2 + 18$.

   5. Plot several points.

   6. Sketch the graph.

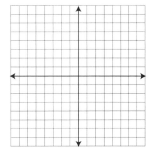

Given $Y = -X^2 + 4X - 4$.

   7. Find the axis of symmetry.

   8. Find the vertex.

   9. Sketch the graph.

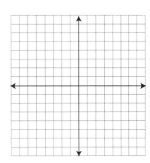

10. Graph $3Y = -3/2\ X^2 + 3$.

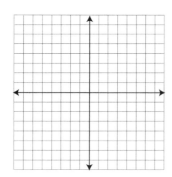

11. Graph $1/2 + 1/4\ Y = 1/8\ X^2$.

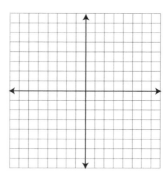

12. Find the center and the radius of $1/2\ (X + 2)^2 + 1/2\ (Y - 3)^2 = 32$.

13. Given the center (–2, –2) and radius (5), create the equation of the circle.

14-15. Find the center and radius of $4X^2 - 32X + 64 + 4Y^2 - 24Y = 0$.

Given points A (–2, 5), B (3, 1), C (–2, –2), and D (4, –4):

16. Compute the distance between points C and D.

17. Find the midpoint between points C and D.

18. What is the slope/intercept equation of the line parallel to $3Y = X - 9$ through (4, 1)?

Given $\dfrac{(X+1)^2}{4} + \dfrac{(Y-2)^2}{9} = 1$:

19. Find the center and the extremities.

20. Graph the figure.

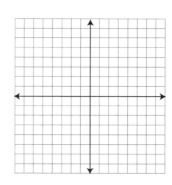

Here are some more application problems that use the equation of a parabola.

Read and solve.

1. A suspension cable that supports a small bridge hangs in a shape similar to a parabola.* The height of the cable in feet is given by $H = 0.2X^2 - 0.5X + 30$. X is the distance from one of the supports to the center (axis of symmetry).

    What is the minimum height of the cable above the bridge at the low point of the curve? Round your answer to the nearest tenth of a foot.

2. A salesman believes that his profit from selling X tickets is given by $P = 50X - 0.2X^2$. What is the maximum profit that he can expect?

*Note: The shape of a cable or chain suspended between two fixed points is actually called a ***catenary curve***. Telephone lines make catenary curves between the poles. The St. Louis Gateway Arch is an example of an inverted catenary curve. The relationships between the weight and length of the chain and the amount of sag can be worked out with advanced calculus.

3. Tommy hit a ball X feet away with a height of $H = -0.002X^2 + 0.5X + 3$. Will this ball clear a 20-foot wall which is 200 feet from where the ball was hit? You may want to make a sketch of this one.

4. A mining company has determined that the cost in dollars per ton to mine a certain ore is given by $C = 0.3X^2 - 3X + 12$. The number of tons of ore that is mined is represented by X. How many tons should be mined to minimize the cost?

5. What is the minimum cost per ton to mine the ore in #4?

For each pair of equations, graph to estimate, and then use substitution or elimination to solve for the points of intersection. You may use a calculator to change radicals to decimals. Round answers to the nearest hundredth.

1. $XY = 12$
    $Y = 2X - 5$

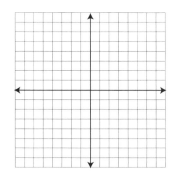

2. $(X - 4)^2 + (Y - 4)^2 = 4$
    $5X = 20$

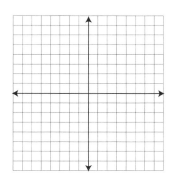

3. $4X^2 + 9Y^2 = 36$
    $Y = -X^2 - 2$

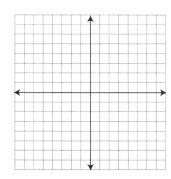

4. $X^2 - 4Y^2 = 16$
   $X^2 + Y^2 = 49$

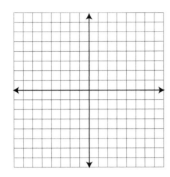

5. $X = 2Y^2 - 5$
   $X = -2Y^2 - 1$

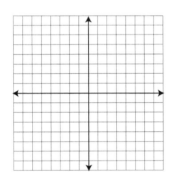

6. $Y = 1/2 X^2 + 3$
   $Y = X + 4$

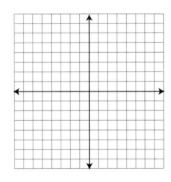

For each pair of equations, graph to estimate, and then use substitution or elimination to solve for the points of intersection. You may use a calculator to change radicals to decimals. Round answers to the nearest hundredth.

1. $Y = X + 4$
$X^2 + Y^2 = 25$

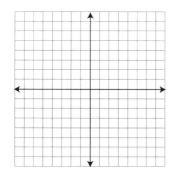

2. $Y = -3$
$Y = -2X^2$

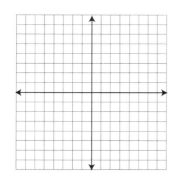

3. $X^2 + Y^2 = 16$
$X^2 + (Y - 6)^2 = 4$

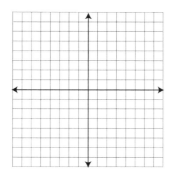

4. $4X^2 + Y^2 = 4$
   $X = Y^2$

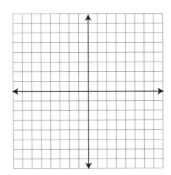

5. $4X^2 - 4Y^2 = 36$
   $Y = X - 1$

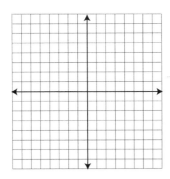

6. $Y = 3X^2$
   $X^2 + Y^2 = 16$

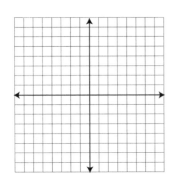

Find the solutions: $\begin{cases} XY = 8 \\ Y = \dfrac{1}{2}X - 2 \end{cases}$

1. Identify the nature of the equations.

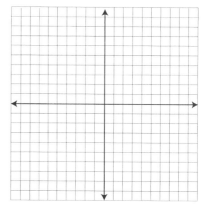

2. Sketch a graph of each to estimate the solutions.

3. Substitute or eliminate to isolate one variable.

4. Solve for the unknown.

5. Solve for the other variable.

6. Give the final solution.

Find the solutions: $\begin{cases} Y = -2x^2 + 3 \\ X = 1 \end{cases}$

7. Identify the nature of the equations.

8. Sketch a graph of each to estimate the solutions.

9. Substitute or eliminate to isolate one variable.

10. Solve for the unknown.

11. Solve for the other variable.

12. Give the final solution.

Find the solutions: $\begin{cases} 75 = 3X^2 + 3Y^2 \\ Y = -2X + 4 \end{cases}$

13. Identify the nature of the equations.

14. Sketch a graph of each to estimate the solutions.

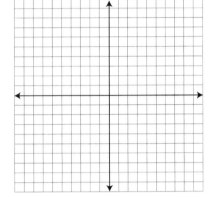

15. Substitute or eliminate to isolate one variable.

16. Solve for the unknown.

17. Solve for the other variable.

18. Give the final solution.

Given points A (–5, 0), B (0, 3), C (3, –2), and D (–2, –4):

19. Compute the distance between points A and B.

20. Find the midpoint between points A and C.

Find the solutions: $\begin{cases} X^2 - Y^2 = 18 \\ X^2 + Y^2 = 32 \end{cases}$

1. Identify the nature of the equations.

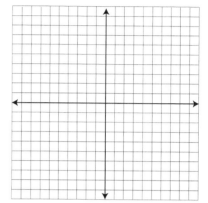

2. Sketch a graph of each to estimate the solutions.

3. Substitute or eliminate to isolate one variable.

4. Solve for the unknown.

5. Solve for the other variable.

6. Give the final solution.

Find the solutions: $\begin{cases} Y = -X^2 + 2X \\ Y = -3 \end{cases}$

7. Identify the nature of the equations.

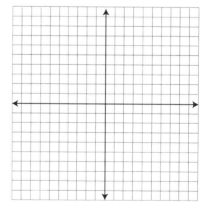

8. Sketch a graph of each to estimate the solutions.

9. Substitute or eliminate to isolate one variable.

10. Solve for the unknown.

11. Solve for the other variable.

12. Give the final solution.

Find the solutions: $\begin{cases} X^2 - Y^2 = 4 \\ 3Y = -X + 3 \end{cases}$

13. Identify the nature of the equations.

14. Sketch a graph of each to estimate the solutions.

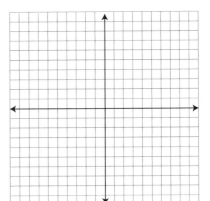

15. Substitute or eliminate to isolate one variable.

16. Solve for the unknown.

17. Solve for the other variable.

18. Give the final solution.

Given points A $(-5, 0)$, B $(0, 3)$, C $(3, -2)$, and D $(-2, -4)$:

19. Compute the distance between points B and D.

20. Find the midpoint between points B and D.

Find the solutions: $\begin{cases} XY = 3 \\ Y = X + 4 \end{cases}$

1. Identify the nature of the equations.

2. Sketch a graph of each to estimate the solutions.

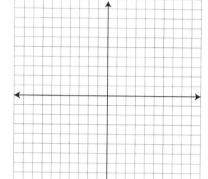

3. Substitute or eliminate to isolate one variable.

4. Solve for the unknown.

5. Solve for the other variable.

6. Give the final solution.

Find the solutions: $\begin{cases} Y = X^2 - 1 \\ Y = -\dfrac{1}{2}X^2 + 3 \end{cases}$

7. Identify the nature of the equations.

8. Sketch a graph of each to estimate the solutions.

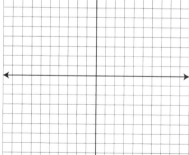

9. Substitute or eliminate to isolate one variable.

10. Solve for the unknown.

11. Solve for the other variable.

12. Give the final solution.

Find the solutions: $\begin{cases} \dfrac{1}{4}X^2 + \dfrac{1}{4}Y^2 = 4 \\ X^2 + (Y + 6)^2 = 9 \end{cases}$

13. Identify the nature of the equations.

14. Sketch a graph of each to estimate the solutions.

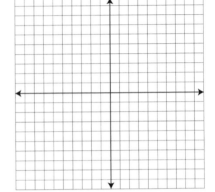

15. Substitute or eliminate to isolate one variable.

16. Solve for the unknown.

17. Solve for the other variable.

18. Give the final solution.

Given A $(-5, 0)$, B $(0, 3)$, C $(3, -2)$, and D $(-2, -4)$:

19. Compute the distance between points A and C.

20. Find the midpoint between points A and C.

You have graphed straight-line inequalities. Conic sections can also involve inequalities. You can follow the same procedure that you used for straight line inequalities to solve conic section inequalities.

First draw the curve just as you would for an equality. Substitute a point from inside the curve into the equation to determine which region to shade. Remember that an inequality should be drawn with a dotted line, but if an equality and an inequality are combined, the line should be solid.

Graph the inequalities.

1. $4X^2 + 4Y^2 \leq 16$

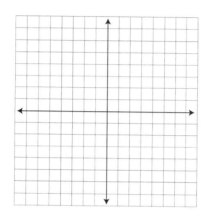

2. $Y > X^2 + 2$

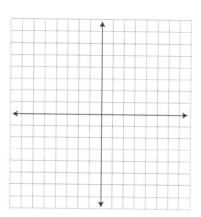

3. $(X - 2)^2 + (Y + 3)^2 \geq 9$

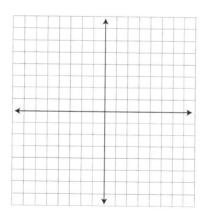

4. $\dfrac{X^2}{9} - \dfrac{Y^2}{4} < 1$

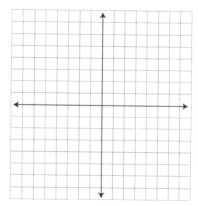

5. XY > −4

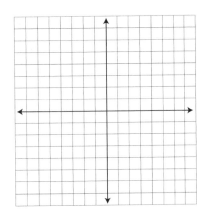

6. $X^2 + Y^2 \geq 25$

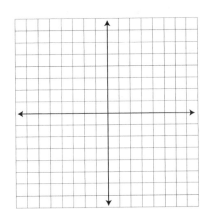

Answer the questions.

1. Justin has seven coins in his pocket. They are all either nickels or dimes. If the total value of the coins is $.45, how many of each kind does he have?

2. Cameron has nickels and pennies. If the value of his 24 coins adds up to $.56, how many of each kind does he have?

3. Nicole has a total of 11 quarters and dimes. If she has $2.15, how many of each coin does she have?

4. Find three consecutive integers such that two times the first integer, plus three times the second integer, minus the third integer, is equal to 21.

5. Find three consecutive even integers such that eight times the first integer, minus two times the third integer, equals 10 plus the second integer.

6. Find three consecutive odd integers such that three times the first integer, plus four times the second integer, equals (-13) times the third integer.

7. The baker has a mixture of 80% wheat flour and 20% oat flour. He also has a mixture that is 90% wheat flour and 10% oat flour. For his new recipe, he needs 10 pounds of a mixture that is 85% wheat flour. How much of each of the original mixtures does he need?

8. A chemist needs 65 ml of a 9% acid solution. He has on hand a 10% acid solution and a 1% acid solution. How many ml of each should he use?

Answer the questions.

1. Drew has a total of 15 nickels and dimes. The value of his coins is $1.15. How many of each coin does he have?

2. Caitlyn found 30 coins while cleaning the house. The coins were either quarters or nickels. If she found $4.30, how many of each coin did she find?

3. Alison's dad gave her a handful of dimes and pennies. If Alison received 14 coins for a total of $.68, how many of each coin was she given?

4. Find three consecutive integers such that four times the first integer, plus eight times the second integer, plus 64, equals four times the third integer.

5. Find three consecutive odd integers such that two times the second integer, minus the first integer, plus 26, equals three times the third integer.

6. Find three consecutive even integers such that three times the first integer, plus six times the second integer, equals eight times the third integer, minus 14.

7. A farmer wants to plant a mixture of 50% alfalfa seed and 50% clover seed in his hay field. He has a seed mixture that is 65% alfalfa and 35% clover, and another that is 45% alfalfa and 55% clover. How much of each mixture should he use to get 60 pounds of the desired seed mixture?

8. A chemical company has an order for 80 liters of a solution of 7% HCl in water. One of its available solutions has 15% HCl, and the other has 5% HCl. How many liters of each solution should be used?

I have 27 coins in my pocket. They are all nickels and pennies. The value of the coins is $.75. How many of each kind do I have?

1. Substitute or eliminate to isolate how many of one coin.

2. Substitute the answer from #1 to find how many of the other coin.

Find three consecutive integers such that four times the third integer, minus five times the first integer, minus the second integer, equals five.

3. Solve for N.

4. Substitute N to find the value of the three integers.

Find three consecutive even integers such that five times the third integer, minus six times the first integer, equals the second integer minus 14.

5. Solve for N.

6. Substitute N to find the value of the three integers.

Find three consecutive odd integers such that nine times the third integer, minus three times the second integer, equals eight times the first integer, plus four.

7. Solve for N.

8. Substitute N to find the value of the three integers.

Kathie has a big cleaning job ahead. She wants 50 gallons of a solution that is 3% Basic H (a detergent) and 97% water. She has some solution left from other jobs. One is 5% Basic H and the other is 2% Basic H. How much of each of these solutions does she need to make the desired solution?

9. Solve for B.

10. Substitute B to find the final amounts.

Do the above problem using the percentages of water instead of the detergent.

11. Solve for W.

12. Substitute W to find the final amounts.

Find the solutions: $\begin{cases} X^2 + Y^2 = 8 \\ 2Y - X^2 = 0 \end{cases}$

13. Identify the nature of the equations.

14. Sketch a graph of each to estimate the solutions.

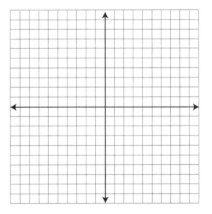

15. Substitute or eliminate to isolate one variable.

16. Solve for the unknown.

17. Solve for the other variable.

18. Give the final solution.

I have 11 coins in my pocket. They are all dimes and nickels. The value of the coins is $.70. How many of each kind do I have?

1. Substitute or eliminate to isolate how many of one coin.

2. Substitute the answer from #1 to find how many of the other coin.

Find three consecutive integers such that five times the second integer, minus seven times the first integer, minus three times the third integer, equals 19.

3. Solve for N.

4. Substitute N to find the value of the three integers.

Find three consecutive even integers such that six times the first integer, minus eight times the second integer, equals 12.

5. Solve for N.

6. Substitute N to find the value of the three integers.

Find three consecutive odd integers such that the sum of them is (-15).

7. Solve for N.

8. Substitute N to find the value of the three integers.

Jeff needs 100 gallons of 4% chlorine and 96% water for his pool. He has two solutions, one that is 7% chlorine and another that is 3% chlorine. How much of each solution is needed in order to make the desired solution?

9. Solve for C.

10. Substitute C to find the final amounts.

Do the above problem using the percentages of water instead of the chlorine.

11. Solve for W.

12. Substitute W to find the final amounts.

Find the solutions: $\begin{cases} Y = -X + 3 \\ XY = -10 \end{cases}$

13. Identify the nature of the equations.

14. Sketch a graph of each to estimate the solutions.

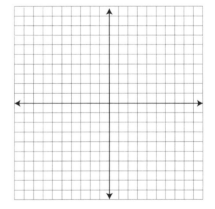

15. Substitute or eliminate to isolate one variable.

16. Solve for the unknown.

17. Solve for the other variable.

18. Give the final solution.

I have 14 coins in my pocket. They are all dimes and quarters. The value of the coins is $2.30. How many of each kind do I have?

1. Substitute or eliminate to isolate how many of one coin.

2. Substitute the answer from #1 to find how many of the other coin.

Find three consecutive integers such that seven times the first integer, plus two times the second integer, equals six times the third integer, plus eight.

3. Solve for N.

4. Substitute N to find the value of the three integers.

Find three consecutive even integers such that three times the first integer, minus seven times the second integer, equals two.

5. Solve for N.

6. Substitute N to find the value of the three integers.

Find three consecutive odd integers such that five times the first integer, minus three times the third integer, equals the second integer plus one.

7. Solve for N.

8. Substitute N to find the value of the three integers.

Rowena needs 20 ml of oil-based paint that is 50% red and 50% mineral spirits. She has some paint that is 60% red and some that is 20% red. How much does she need of each to make the desired paint?

9. Solve for R.

10. Substitute R to find the final amounts.

Do the above problem using the percentages of mineral spirits instead of the colorant.

11. Solve for M.

12. Substitute M to find the final amounts.

Find the solutions: $\begin{cases} 2(X + 2)^2 + 2(Y - 1)^2 = 18 \\ X = -4 \end{cases}$

13. Identify the nature of the equations.

14. Sketch a graph of each to estimate the solutions.

15. Substitute or eliminate to isolate one variable.

16. Solve for the unknown.

17. Solve for the other variable.

18. Give the final solution.

The solution to a system of equations is the list of **points** where the graphs of the equations intersect. The solution to a system of inequalities is the list of **regions** that are common to both. If there are no regions that intersect, we say that there are no real-number solutions.

Graph the systems of inequalities. Shade your graph so that the solution region for each system is clear.

1. $4X^2 + Y^2 < 16$
   $X^2 + Y^2 \geq 4$

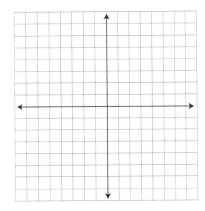

2. $4X^2 + Y^2 \geq 16$
   $X^2 + Y^2 \leq 4$

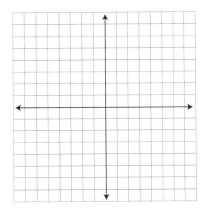

3. $X > Y^2 - 2$
   $X > 3$

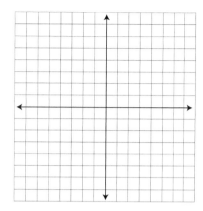

4. $Y^2 - X^2 < 16$
   $X < -2$

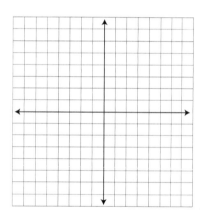

Answer the questions.

1. Richard is five times as old as David. In five years, Richard will be three times as old as David. How old are Richard and David now?

2. Next year, Joanne will be six times Nicole's age. In seven years, Nicole will be one-third the age of Joanne. How old is each girl now?

3. Two years ago, Tyler's dad was two times Tyler's age. In 23 years, Tyler will be two-thirds the age of his dad. How old is each one now?

4. In five years, Carol will be six times the age of Heather. In two more years after that, Heather will be one-fifth the age of Carol. How old are Carol and Heather now?

5. A boat travels at a rate of 12 mph without any current. The boat went downstream for two hours, and then turned around and returned to the starting point in six hours. How far did the boat travel each way, and what is the speed of the current?

6. A bird flew with the wind for three hours and covered a distance of 36 miles. Then it turned around and flew against the wind, going two miles in one hour before stopping to rest. What was the speed of the bird and the speed of the wind?

7. A barge can go 21 miles downstream in the same time it goes 9 miles upstream. The rate of the water is 2 mph. What is the rate of the barge?

8. An airplane flew between two cities at a speed of 200 mph. With the wind behind the plane, the trip took 9 hours. The return trip was against the wind and took 11 hours. What was the distance between the cities and the speed of the wind?

Answer the questions.

1. Last year, Sally was two times the age of Jane. In 19 years, Jane will be two-thirds the age of Sally. How old is each now?

2. Sue is three times the age of Bethany. In 30 years, Bethany will be three-fifths the age of Sue. How old is each one now?

3. Ten years ago, Sam was one-sixth the age of Carlos. Today, Carlos is four times Sam's age. How old is each person now?

4. June is one-half the age of Juanita. In 15 years, she will be five-sevenths of Juanita's age. How old is each person today?

5. The current was 2 mph. A fish swam downstream for 25 miles, and then turned around and swam against the current for 35 miles to its spawning place. The upstream trip took seven times as long as the downstream trip. What was the speed of the fish?

6. Aragorn paddled 12 miles upstream in the same amount of time it took him to paddle 60 miles downstream. The rate of the current is 4 mph. What was the rate at which he paddled, and the total time of his trip?

7. A small plane flew at a speed of 100 mph. It took six hours to get to its destination flying with the wind, and nine hours to return against the wind. How far away was the plane's destination, and what was the wind speed?

8. David thought he could increase the efficiency of his car by using a sail arrangement. He drove 240 miles in four hours with the wind pushing his sail. When he made the return trip against the wind, he was only able to make 160 miles in four hours, although the car's engine speed was the same. What was the speed of the car and the speed of the wind?

In two years, Phil will be twice as old as Evan. Sixteen years ago, Phil was four and one-quarter times the age of Evan. How old is each one now?

1. Choose the variables and write the first equation from the information given.

2. Using the same variables, write the second equation from the information given.

3. Isolate and solve for the value of one variable by substitution.

4. Use the answer from #3 to solve for the value of the other variable.

Keith is two and three-quarters times the age of Melody. Two years ago, Melody was one-third the age of Keith. How old is each one now?

5. Choose the variables and write the first equation from the information given.

6. Using the same variables, write the second equation from the information given.

7. Isolate and solve for the value of one variable by substitution.

8. Use the answer from #7 to solve for the value of the other variable.

Noah took four hours to go 36 miles downstream. Later that same day, it took him three hours to cover 15 miles upstream. What is the rate of the current and the rate of the boat?

9. Choose the variables and write the first equation from the information given.

10. Using the same variables, write the second equation from the information given.

11. Isolate and solve for the value of one variable by substitution.

12. Use the answer from #11 to solve for the value of the other variable.

I have 24 coins in my pocket. They are all pennies and nickels. The value of the coins is $.72. How many of each kind are there?

13. Substitute or eliminate to isolate how many of one coin.

14. Substitute the answer from #13 to find how many of the other coin.

Find three consecutive integers such that four times the third integer, minus eight times the second integer, equals nine times the first integer.

15. Solve for N.

16. Substitute N to find the value of the three integers.

Find three consecutive even integers such that the sum of them is 84.

17. Solve for N.

18. Substitute N to find the value of the three integers.

Linn is looking for an ideal colloidal mineral solution. He has two solutions. The first is 20% minerals and the second is 5% minerals. He wants 12 ounces of a 15% mineral solution. How much of each of his solutions does he need?

19. Solve for C.

20. Substitute C to find the final amounts.

Last year, Steven was one-half the age of Katie. In seven years, Katie will be one and a half times the age of Steven. How old is each one now?

1. Choose the variables and write the first equation from the information given.

2. Using the same variables, write the second equation from the information given.

3. Isolate and solve for the value of one variable by substitution.

4. Use the answer from #3 to solve for the value of the other variable.

Last year, Kimberly was one-half the age of Danny. In 11 years, Danny will be one and a half times the age of Kimberly. How old are they now?

5. Choose the variables and write the first equation from the information given.

6. Using the same variables, write the second equation from the information given.

7. Isolate and solve for the value of one variable by substitution.

8. Use the answer from #7 to solve for the value of the other variable.

It took Natty Bumpo one hour to go 24 miles headed upstream, but he went 48 miles downstream in the same amount of time. What is the rate of the current and the rate of the boat?

9. Choose the variables, and write the first equation from the information given.

10. Using the same variables, write the second equation from the information given.

11. Isolate and solve for the value of one variable by substitution.

12. Use the answer from #11 to solve for the value of the other variable.

I have 19 coins in my pocket. They are all dimes and nickels. The value of the coins is $1.30. How many of each kind do I have?

13. Substitute or eliminate to isolate how many of one coin.

14. Substitute the answer from #13 to find how many of the other coin.

Find three consecutive integers such that three times the first integer, minus five times the second integer, equals three, plus two times the third integer.

15. Solve for N.

16. Substitute N to find the value of the three integers.

Find three consecutive even integers such that eight times the third integer equals five times the first integer, minus 28.

17. Solve for N.

18. Substitute N to find the value of the three integers.

Cal has the big job of cleaning the garage. He needs 90 ml of mixture that is 20% Basic H and the rest water. He has two solutions already made that are 25% and 10% Basic H. How much of each of these liquids will he use to form the required solution?

19. Solve for C.

20. Substitute C to find the final amounts.

Bob was 30 when Derrick was born. In 10 years, he will be twice as old as Derrick. How old is each one now?

1. Choose the variables and write the first equation from the information given.

2. Using the same variables, write the second equation from the information given.

3. Isolate and solve for the value of one variable by substitution.

4. Use the answer from #3 to solve for the value of the other variable.

Lindsey is five times the age of Kim. Two years ago, Kim was one-ninth the age of Lindsey. How old is each one now?

5. Choose the variables and write the first equation from the information given.

6. Using the same variables, write the second equation from the information given.

7. Isolate and solve for the value of one variable by substitution.

8. Use the answer from #7 to solve for the value of the other variable.

Warren paddled for five hours in order to complete the 65 miles downstream. Paddling upstream, it took him eight hours to make 24 miles. What is the rate of the current and the rate of the boat?

9. Choose the variables and write the first equation from the information given.

10. Using the same variables, write the second equation from the information given.

11. Isolate and solve for the value of one variable by substitution.

12. Use the answer from #11 to solve for the value of the other variable.

I have 12 coins in my pocket. They are all dimes and quarters. The value of the coins is $2.55. How many of each kind do I have?

13. Substitute or eliminate to isolate how many of one coin.

14. Substitute the answer from #13 to find how many of the other coin.

Find three consecutive integers such that six times the third integer, plus eight, equals eight times the second integer, minus the first integer.

15. Solve for N.

16. Substitute N to find the value of the three integers.

Find three consecutive odd integers such that the sum of them is (−51).

17. Solve for N.

18. Substitute N to find the value of the three integers.

Nancy is making a window-cleaning solution and needs 80 ml of mixture that is 6% alcohol and the rest water. She has two solutions already made that are 3% and 8% alcohol. How much of each of these liquids will she use to make the required solution?

19. Solve for C.

20. Substitute C to find the final amounts.

Mixture problems are similar to the motion problems you have been solving. Put all your information in terms of one unknown and set up an equation. It can be helpful to make a chart of all the known information before starting to solve the problem.

Example 1

How many pounds of walnuts that cost $3.00 per pound must be mixed with 20 pounds of almonds that cost $5.00 per pound to make a mixture that costs $3.50 per pound? (pounds of walnuts = X, pounds of almonds = 20, pounds of mixture = X + 20)

	amount	cost per unit	value
walnuts	X	3.00	3.00X
almonds	20	5.00	100
mixture	X + 20	3.50	3.50(X + 20)

$3.00X + 100 = 3.50(X + 20)$ Add the values of walnuts and almonds to find the value of the final mixture.

$3X + 100 = 3.5X + 70$ Simplify and solve for X.

$30 = .5X$

$60 = X$ The mixture must contain 60 pounds of walnuts.

Fill in the chart and solve. Round answers involving money to the nearest cent.

1. Low-grade hamburger at $2.00 per pound was added to 50 pounds of ground round priced at $3.75 per pound. The new mixture of meat will be sold at $2.50 per pound. How much low-grade hamburger was added to the mixture?

	amount	cost per unit	value
low grade			
ground round			
mixture			

2. Twelve pounds of metal worth $2.00 a pound were melted and mixed with 12 pounds of another metal. If the resulting mixture was worth $1.25 per pound, what was the price per pound of the second metal?

	amount	cost per unit	value
first metal			
second metal			
mixture			

3. A health-food store made a mixture of 100 pounds of wheat flour and 50 pounds of corn-meal flour and sold it in 5-pound bags for $4.75 a bag. Separately, the price per pound of the corn meal is twice the price of the wheat flour. What is the individual cost per pound of each kind of flour?

	amount	cost per unit	value
wheat			
corn			
mixture			

Find the solution that will satisfy all three variables.

    A. $3X + 6Y - 4Z = 17$ B. $-X + 5Y + 4Z = 11$ C. $2X + 2Y - 10Z = 0$

1. Choose two equations and eliminate one variable.

2. Choose two different equations and eliminate the same variable.

3. Now take the results of #1 and #2, eliminate another variable, and solve.

4. Take the result of #3, substitute it into one of the equations from #1 or #2, and solve.

5. Take the results of #3 and #4, substitute them into one of A, B, or C, and solve.

6. Check your solution set in A, B, and C.

Find the solution that will satisfy all three variables.

    A. $-3X - Y - 2Z = -13$ B. $2X + 2Y + Z = 16$ C. $X + 3Y + 3Z = 13$

7. Choose two equations and eliminate one variable.

8. Choose two different equations and eliminate the same variable.

9. Now take the results of #7 and #8, eliminate another variable, and solve.

10. Take the result of #9, substitute it into one of the equations from #7 or #8, and solve the equation.

11. Take the results of #9 and #10, substitute them into one of A, B, or C, and solve.

12. Check your solution set in A, B, and C.

Find the solution that will satisfy all three variables.

    A. $4X + 6Y + 2Z = 22$ B. $-4X + 3Y - 4Z = -10$ C. $5X + 4Y - 3Z = 4$

13. Choose two equations and eliminate one variable.

14. Choose two different equations and eliminate the same variable.

15. Now take the results of #13 and #14, eliminate another variable, and solve.

16. Take the result of #15, substitute it into one of the equations from #7 or #8, and solve the equation.

17. Take the results of #15 and #16, substitute them into one of A, B, or C, and solve.

18. Check your solution set in A, B, and C.

Find the solution that will satisfy all three variables.

 A. $4X - 4Y + 2Z = -2$ B. $5X + Y + 2Z = 1$ C. $X + 6Y - 3Z = -11$

1. Choose two equations and eliminate one variable.

2. Choose two different equations and eliminate the same variable.

3. Now take the results of #1 and #2, eliminate another variable, and solve.

4. Take the result of #3, substitute it into one of the equations from #1 or #2, and solve the equation.

5. Take the results of #3 and #4, substitute them into one of A, B, or C, and solve.

6. Check your solution set in A, B, and C.

Find the solution that will satisfy all three variables.

 A. $X + 2Y + 3Z = 32$ B. $4X - 3Y + Z = 7$ C. $-2X + 6Y - 2Z = 4$

7. Choose two equations and eliminate one variable.

8. Choose two different equations and eliminate the same variable.

9. Now take the results of #7 and #8, eliminate another variable, and solve.

10. Take the result of #9, substitute it into one of the equations from #7 or #8, and solve the equation.

11. Take the results of #9 and #10, substitute them into one of A, B, or C, and solve.

12. Check your solution set in A, B, and C.

Find the solution that will satisfy all three variables.

A. $X - 8Y + Z = 6$ B. $2X + 7Y - Z = 11$ C. $2X - 10Y - 3Z = -22$

13. Choose two equations and eliminate one variable.

14. Choose two different equations and eliminate the same variable.

15. Now take the results of #13 and #14, eliminate another variable, and solve.

16. Take the result of #15, substitute it into one of the equations from #7 or #8, and solve the equation.

17. Take the results of #15 and #16, substitute them into one of A, B, or C, and solve.

18. Check your solution set in A, B, and C.

Find the solution that will satisfy all three variables.

A. $5X - 3Y + 3Z = 3$ B. $2X - 6Y - 4Z = 2$ C. $3X - 5Y + Z = -3$

1. Choose two equations and eliminate one variable.

2. Choose two different equations and eliminate the same variable.

3. Now take the results of #1 and #2, eliminate another variable, and solve.

4. Take the result of #3, substitute it into one of the equations from #1 or #2, and solve the equation.

5. Take the results of #3 and #4, substitute them into one of A, B, or C, and solve.

6. Check your solution set in A, B, and C.

Find the solution that will satisfy all three variables.

A. $3X + 2Y + 4Z = 9$ B. $4X + 3Y - 2Z = 6$ C. $5X + 4Y - 3Z = 8$

7. Choose two equations and eliminate one variable.

8. Choose two different equations and eliminate the same variable.

9. Now take the results of #7 and #8, eliminate another variable, and solve.

10. Take the result of #9, substitute it into one of the equations from #7 or #8, and solve the equation.

11. Take the results of #9 and #10, substitute them into one of A, B, or C, and solve.

12. Check your solution set in A, B, and C.

Three years ago, Pat was four times the age of Claire. Pat was 33 when Claire was born. How old are Claire and Pat now?

13. Choose the variables and write the first equation from the information given.

14. Using the same variables write the second equation from the information given.

15. Isolate and solve for the value of one variable by substitution.

16. Use the answer from #15 to solve for the value of the other variable.

Jonah took two hours to go 34 miles downstream. On the same river headed upstream, it took him three hours to make 15 miles. What is the rate of the current and the rate of the boat?

17. Choose the variables and write the first equation from the information given.

18. Using the same variables write the second equation from the information given.

19. Isolate and solve for the value of one variable by substitution.

20. Use the answer from #19 to solve for the value of the other variable.

Find the solution that will satisfy all three variables.

$\quad$ A. $\ 6X + 3Y - 5Z = 5 \qquad$ B. $\ -2X - 3Y - Z = -1 \qquad$ C. $\ 4X + 2Y - 6Z = -2$

1. Choose two equations and eliminate one variable.

2. Choose two different equations and eliminate the same variable.

3. Now take the results of #1 and #2, eliminate another variable, and solve.

4. Take the result of #3, substitute it into one of the equations from #1 or #2, and solve the equation.

5. Take the results of #3 and #4, substitute them into one of A, B, or C, and solve.

6. Check your solution set in A, B, and C.

Find the solution that will satisfy all three variables.

$\quad$ A. $\ X - 2Y + 4Z = -4 \qquad$ B. $\ 3X + 4Y - 5Z = 25 \qquad$ C. $\ 5X - 3Y + 2Z = 12$

7. Choose two equations and eliminate one variable.

8. Choose two different equations and eliminate the same variable.

9. Now take the results of #7 and #8, eliminate another variable, and solve.

10. Take the result of #9, substitute it into one of the equations from #7 or #8, and solve the equation.

11. Take the results of #9 and #10, substitute them into one of A, B, or C, and solve.

12. Check your solution set in A, B, and C.

Next year, Sharon will be twice as old as Gretchen. Five years ago, Gretchen was four-ninths the age of Sharon. How old is each person now?

13. Choose the variables and write the first equation from the information given.

14. Using the same variables write the second equation from the information given.

15. Isolate and solve for the value of one variable by substitution.

16. Use the answer from #15 to solve for the value of the other variable.

Davy Crockett took three hours to go 42 miles downstream. Headed upstream, it took him five hours to make 30 miles. What is the rate of the current and the rate of the boat?

17. Choose the variables and write the first equation from the information given.

18. Using the same variables write the second equation from the information given.

19. Isolate and solve for the value of one variable by substitution.

20. Use the answer from #19 to solve for the value of the other variable.

Find the solution that will satisfy all three variables.

A. $-2X + 3Y + 5Z = -7$ B. $-6X - 2Y - Z = -15$ C. $-4X + 4Y + 5Z = -15$

1.   Choose two equations and eliminate one variable.

2.   Choose two different equations and eliminate the same variable.

3.   Now take the results of #1 and #2, eliminate another variable, and solve.

4.   Take the result of #3, substitute it into one of the equations from #1 or #2, and solve the equation.

5.   Take the results of #3 and #4, substitute them into one of A, B, or C, and solve.

6.   Check your solution set in A, B, and C.

Find the solution that will satisfy all three variables.

A. $2X - 5Y + 2Z = -5$ B. $-3X + 4Y - 4Z = 6$ C. $5X + 6Y - Z = 18$

7.   Choose two equations and eliminate one variable.

8.   Choose two different equations and eliminate the same variable.

9.   Now take the results of #7 and #8, eliminate another variable, and solve.

10. Take the result of #9, substitute it into one of the equations from #7 or #8, and solve the equation.

11. Take the results of #9 and #10, substitute them into one of A, B, or C, and solve.

12. Check your solution set in A, B, and C.

In 15 years, Wallace will be one and four-tenths the age of Cindy. Five years ago, Cindy was six-tenths the age of Wallace. How old are they now?

13. Choose the variables and write the first equation from the information given.

14. Using the same variables write the second equation from the information given.

15. Isolate and solve for the value of one variable by substitution.

16. Use the answer from #15 to solve for the value of the other variable.

Wetzel paddled two hours to traverse 20 miles downstream. Headed upstream, it took him five hours to cover the same distance. What is the rate of the current and the rate of the boat?

17. Choose the variables and write the first equation from the information given.

18. Using the same variables write the second equation from the information given.

19. Isolate and solve for the value of one variable by substitution.

20. Use the answer from #19 to solve for the value of the other variable.

Here are some more application problems similar to those in 25H and 26H. You will be solving for maximum or minimum values. These are more challenging because you have to set up the equations for yourself. There is a little extra information in #1 to get you started. Finish the first problem, and check your answer before trying the others.

Read and solve.

1. FunTrip Bus Lines has advertised a group outing. If 20 people sign up, the cost is $80.00 per person. For every extra person beyond 20, the ticket price will drop by $2.00 per person. The bus can accommodate 30 people. How many people will maximize the revenues of FunTrip Bus Lines? What is the total revenue for the trip if the optimum number of people sign up for the trip?

   Let X be the number of people beyond 20 who sign up for the trip.
   Revenue (R) = number of people times total ticket prices
   Number of people on trip = 20 + X
   Ticket price = 80 – 2X

2. Farmer Jones has a bull calf that currently weighs 500 pounds and is gaining 20 pounds per week. He could sell this calf right now for 90¢ per pound. As he waits, the price of beef falls 3¢ a pound each week. In order to maximize his profits, how many weeks should Farmer Jones wait before he sells his calf? (Let the unknown be W, or the number of weeks he should wait.)

   How much money will the farmer receive for the calf if he maximizes his profits?*

   *This problem has been simplified—in real life the cost of feeding the animal would have to be included, and possibly other costs as well!

3. A toll bridge averages 100,000 cars a day with a toll of $3.00 per car. There is a free bridge several miles away. Traffic across the toll bridge is believed to drop by 5,000 cars per day for every 50¢ increase in the toll. What toll would maximize revenues? What would the total revenue be at that rate?

4. A citrus grower plants 30 trees per acre, and can harvest 20 bushels of fruit per tree. If he plants his trees closer together, he will lose one-third of a bushel per tree for every extra tree he adds, as long as he does not exceed 18 additional trees per acre. How many trees should he plant per acre in order to maximize the yield?

The limit of 18 additional trees per acre is a common-sense limit for the grower. As long as your answer for the number of additional trees is under 18, you do not need to worry about this value.

Add the one-dimensional vectors.

1. $\xrightarrow{\ \ +5\ \ }$ $\xleftarrow{\ \ -8\ \ }$

2.

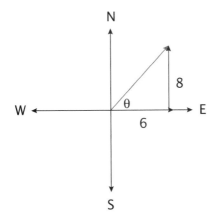

Follow the directions.

3. Give the two components of a vector.

4. Tom traveled six miles east and eight miles north. Use the Pythagorean theorem to find the distance from his starting point to his ending point. Your answer is the magnitude of the resultant vector.

5. Using the triangle below, fill in the blanks and find the trig ratios of θ (theta).

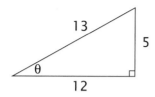

sin θ = ─────────── = ───── = ───────
           hypotenuse

cos θ = ─ adjacent ── = ───── = ───────

tan θ = ─────────── = ───── = ───────

6. Using the inverse of the sine function, find the measure of angle θ in the triangle shown in #5.

7. Cindy left her home and drove 5 miles due east and then 10 miles due north to get to the grocery store. What is her distance and direction from her starting point? (Round distances in this lesson to the nearest hundredth and degrees to the nearest tenth.)

8. A boat sails 100 miles east and then 40 miles north. Give the distance and direction of the boat from its starting point.

Follow the directions.

1. Name the three trig ratios, and tell what sides of the triangle are used to find each one.

2. The two components of a vector are _____ and _____ .

3. A vector found by combining two vectors is the _____ vector.

4. Aiden traveled 3 miles east and 11 miles north. Use the Pythagorean theorem to find the magnitude of the resultant vector.

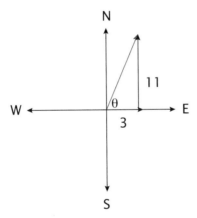

5. Using the triangle above, fill in the blanks and find the trig ratios of θ. Round the decimal form of each ratio to four places.

sin θ = —————— = —————— = ————

cos θ = —————— = —————— = ————

tan θ = —————— = —————— = ————

6. Using the inverse of the tan ratio, find the measure of angle θ in the triangle on the previous page. This tells the direction of Aiden's resultant vector in #4.

7. A boat sailed 100 miles west and 10 miles north. What is the magnitude and direction of the resultant vector?

8. The first vector is (+4) on the X-axis and (+3) on the Y-axis. The second vector is (+2) on the X-axis and (+1) on the Y-axis. Draw a sketch and find the sum of the two vectors.

9. Find the magnitude and the direction of the final vector in #8.

Follow the directions.

1. A man walked 30 miles east and then 40 miles north. How far is the man from his starting point? In what direction could he have walked to reach the ending point directly?

2. The first vector is (+8) on the X-axis and (+2) on the Y-axis. The second vector is (–5) on the X-axis and (+3) on the Y-axis. What is the sum of the two vectors? Find the magnitude and the direction of the final vector.

3. Sketch the graph of $Y - X^2 = 0$.

4. Sketch the graph of $2X + Y < 2$.

5. Sketch the graph of $XY = -4$.

6. Find the slope between (1, –2) and (–3, –5).

7. Simplify $2\sqrt{-24} + 3\sqrt{8}$.

8. Factor $X^2 - 16X + 64$.

9. Simplify $\dfrac{X^2 - \dfrac{2}{X}}{X - \dfrac{3}{X}}$.

10. Solve $X^2 - 2X - 7 = 0$.

Follow the directions.

1. A plane flew 75 miles east and 125 miles north. What are the direction and magnitude of the resultant vector?

2. The first vector is (–4) on the X-axis and (+2) on the Y-axis. The second vector is (–1) on the X-axis and (+6) on the Y-axis. What is the sum of the two vectors? Find the magnitude and direction of the final vector.

3. Sketch the graph of $X^2 + Y^2 = 16$.

4. Sketch the graph of $X \geq -3 + Y$.

5. Sketch the graph of $X^2 - Y^2 = 4$.

6. Find the equation of the line in slope-intercept form if the slope is $\left(+\frac{1}{2}\right)$, and a point on the line is (3, 4).

7. Simplify $\dfrac{2\sqrt{12}}{\sqrt{10}}$.

8. Factor $6X^2 - X - 2$.

9. Simplify $\dfrac{\dfrac{1}{X} - 2}{\dfrac{4}{X}}$.

10. Solve $2X^2 - 3X = 2$.

Follow the directions.

1. An ant crawled 15 feet east and 30 feet north. What direction and distance would have brought the ant most directly to the same point?

2. The first vector is (–8) on the X-axis and (+6) on the Y-axis. The second vector is (+2) on the X-axis and (–3) on the Y-axis. What is the sum of the two vectors? Find the magnitude and direction of the final vector.

3. Sketch the graph of $X - Y^2 = 0$.

4. Graph $Y = \sqrt{X}$. (Hint: Plot points using only positive values of the square root.)

5. Graph $4X^2 + 9Y^2 = 36$.

6. Find the distance between (1, –2) and (–3, 6).

7. Simplify $\dfrac{4}{\sqrt{3}} + \dfrac{6\sqrt{2}}{\sqrt{5}}$.

8. Factor $10X^2 + 23X + 12$.

9. Simplify $3B^{-2}A^3C - \dfrac{2C}{B^2A^{-3}} + \dfrac{7CB^2}{A^{-3}}$.

10. Solve $X^2 + X + 1 = 0$.

You have solved systems of equations by using elimination. Now we are going to find the pattern, and then find the algebraic equation that represents this pattern.

We will start by reviewing a problem with real numbers, and then move to variables to reveal the pattern and formula.

Example 1

Equation $\boxed{Q}$: $4X + 5Y = 7$

Equation $\boxed{P}$: $2X + 3Y = 5$

To eliminate the Xs and solve for Y, multiply equation Q by 2 and equation P by 4.

$\boxed{Q}$ $2 \cdot 4X + 2 \cdot 5Y = 2 \cdot 7$

$\boxed{P}$ $4 \cdot 2X + 4 \cdot 3Y = 4 \cdot 5$ Keep the original coefficients intact.

$2 \cdot 5Y - 4 \cdot 3Y = 2 \cdot 7 - 4 \cdot 5$ Now subtract equation P from equation Q to solve using elimination.

$Y(2 \cdot 5 - 4 \cdot 3) = (2 \cdot 7 - 4 \cdot 5)$ Solve for Y.

$Y = \dfrac{2 \cdot 7 - 4 \cdot 5}{2 \cdot 5 - 4 \cdot 3} = \dfrac{14 - 20}{10 - 12} = \dfrac{-6}{-2} = 3$

To eliminate the Ys and solve for X, multiply equation P by 5, and equation Q by 3.

$\boxed{P}$ $5 \cdot 2X + 5 \cdot 3Y = 5 \cdot 5$

$\boxed{Q}$ $3 \cdot 4X + 3 \cdot 5Y = 3 \cdot 7$ Keep the original coefficients intact.

$5 \cdot 2X - 3 \cdot 4X = 5 \cdot 5 - 3 \cdot 7$ Now subtract equation Q from equation P.

$X(5 \cdot 2 - 3 \cdot 4) = 5 \cdot 5 - 3 \cdot 7$ Solve for X.

$X = \dfrac{5 \cdot 5 - 3 \cdot 7}{5 \cdot 2 - 3 \cdot 4} = \dfrac{25 - 21}{10 - 12} = \dfrac{4}{-2} = -2$

Now we'll use variables for the coefficients and run through the same procedure.

Example 2

Equation $\boxed{P}$: AX + BY = E

Equation $\boxed{Q}$: CX + DY = F

To eliminate the Xs and solve for Y, multiply equation P by C and equation Q by A.

$\boxed{Q}$ $A \cdot CX + A \cdot DY = A \cdot F$

$\boxed{P}$ $C \cdot AX + C \cdot BY = C \cdot E$

$A \cdot DY - C \cdot BY = A \cdot F - C \cdot E$ Now subtract equation P from equation Q.

$Y(A \cdot D - C \cdot B) = (A \cdot F - C \cdot E)$ Solve for Y.

$$Y = \frac{A \cdot F - C \cdot E}{A \cdot D - C \cdot B}$$

To eliminate the Ys and solve for X, multiply equation P by D and equation Q by B.

$\boxed{P}$ $D \cdot AX + D \cdot BY = D \cdot E$

$\boxed{Q}$ $B \cdot CX + B \cdot DY = B \cdot F$

$D \cdot AX - B \cdot CX = D \cdot E - B \cdot F$ Now subtract equation Q from equation P.

$X(D \cdot A - B \cdot C) = (D \cdot E - B \cdot F)$ Solve for X.

$$X = \frac{D \cdot E - B \cdot F}{D \cdot A - B \cdot C}$$

Now we have a formula to solve equations with two variables. There is another way to write this without variables cluttering up the formula. An array or collection of numbers can be arranged and written as a *matrix*. Using example 1, we can choose the coefficients and write them in a matrix with two horizontal rows and two vertical columns. Matrices (plural of matrix) are usually enclosed with parentheses or braces.

$$\begin{pmatrix} 2 & 3 \\ 4 & 5 \end{pmatrix} \qquad \text{Matrices} \qquad \begin{Bmatrix} 2 & 3 \\ 4 & 5 \end{Bmatrix}$$

This is a neat and efficient way of organizing the data, but it does not tell you what to do with it. If you replace the braces or parentheses with two vertical lines, the matrix turns into a determinant that dictates an operation to be performed with the numbers. This is similar to what would happen if you saw a "5" and a "3" on a piece of paper. The data is there, but you don't know what to do with it. If an "x" appeared between the numbers, you would know to multiply them.

Just as "x" is the symbol for multiplication, the vertical bars are the symbol for a **determinant**. The determinant in example 3 multiplies the 2 times the 5, and then subtracts the 4 times the 3. Think of a ribbon starting at the 2 and going down through the 5, looping around to the left and going up through the 4 and the 3. Study the picture and the examples closely.

Example 3

Determinant $\begin{vmatrix} 2 & 3 \\ 4 & 5 \end{vmatrix}$
$\begin{vmatrix} 2 & 3 \\ 4 & 5 \end{vmatrix} = 2 \cdot 5 - 4 \cdot 3 = 10 - 12 = -2$

Example 4

Determinant $\begin{vmatrix} A & B \\ C & D \end{vmatrix}$
$\begin{vmatrix} A & B \\ C & D \end{vmatrix} = A \cdot D - C \cdot B = AD - CB$

Go back to our solution in example 2 and see how all this comes together. The solutions for X and Y can be written as fractions with determinants in the numerators and denominators. This formula is called Cramer's Rule.

$$X = \frac{\begin{vmatrix} E & B \\ F & D \end{vmatrix}}{\begin{vmatrix} A & B \\ C & D \end{vmatrix}} = \frac{ED - FB}{AD - CB} \qquad Y = \frac{\begin{vmatrix} A & E \\ C & F \end{vmatrix}}{\begin{vmatrix} A & B \\ C & D \end{vmatrix}} = \frac{AF - CE}{AD - CB}$$

There is a technique to finding which determinant goes with X and which goes with Y. Looking at examples 1 and 2, you will see that the denominator is the same in each fraction. It is the result of subtracting two factors made up of the coefficients of X and Y. In other words, DA – BC or AD – CB (which are the same thing). So the denominator in both cases looks like this:

$$\begin{vmatrix} A & B \\ C & D \end{vmatrix}$$

The numerator is the same as the denominator, except that for X, the first column $\begin{smallmatrix} A \\ C \end{smallmatrix}$ is replaced with the constants $\begin{smallmatrix} E \\ F \end{smallmatrix}$. Since we always write the X first in an ordered pair, we can remember that the first column is replaced with the constants.

Y is always written second, and in the numerator of the Y fraction, the second column $\begin{smallmatrix} B \\ D \end{smallmatrix}$ is replaced with the constants $\begin{smallmatrix} E \\ F \end{smallmatrix}$.

Example 5

Here is example 1 solved with determinants.

$2X + 3Y = 5 \qquad 4X + 5Y = 7$

$$X = \frac{\begin{vmatrix} 5 & 3 \\ 7 & 5 \end{vmatrix}}{\begin{vmatrix} 2 & 3 \\ 4 & 5 \end{vmatrix}} = \frac{25 - 21}{10 - 12} = -2 \qquad Y = \frac{\begin{vmatrix} 2 & 5 \\ 4 & 7 \end{vmatrix}}{\begin{vmatrix} 2 & 3 \\ 4 & 5 \end{vmatrix}} = \frac{14 - 20}{10 - 12} = 3$$

Use Cramer's Rule to solve the systems of equations.

1. $-4X + 3Y = 2$
    $-2X + Y = -6$

2. $3X - Y = 1$
    $3X + 4Y = -19$

3. $X + 4Y = 11$
    $-3X + 2Y = 9$

There is also a formula for solving systems of equations with three variables using determinants. In this case, there are three rows and three columns. The formula has three diagonals that are positive and three diagonals that are negative for each of three unknowns or variables. The denominator is the same for each unknown, but the solution is still a lot of work. Study Cramer's rule for three variables, and then observe the example closely.

In order to get three full diagonals down and three up, first extend the three-columned matrix by copying the first two columns to the right, as shown by the outlined letters in the figure. The downward diagonals are added, and the upward diagonals are subtracted, as before.

$$\begin{vmatrix} A & B & C \\ D & E & F \\ G & H & J \end{vmatrix}$$

$$\begin{vmatrix} A & B & C \\ D & E & F \\ G & H & J \end{vmatrix}\begin{matrix} A & B \\ D & E \\ G & H \end{matrix} = AEJ + BFG + CDH - GEC - HFA - JDB$$

Example 6

$$AX + BY + CZ = K \qquad DX + EY + FZ = L \qquad GX + HY + JZ = M$$

$$X = \frac{\begin{vmatrix} K & B & C \\ L & E & F \\ M & H & J \end{vmatrix}\begin{matrix} K & B \\ L & E \\ M & H \end{matrix}}{\begin{vmatrix} A & B & C \\ D & E & F \\ G & H & J \end{vmatrix}\begin{matrix} A & B \\ D & E \\ G & H \end{matrix}} = \frac{KEJ + BFM + CLH - MEC - HFK - JLB}{AEJ + BFG + CDH - GEC - HFA - JDB}$$

$$Y = \frac{\begin{vmatrix} A & K & C \\ D & L & F \\ G & M & J \end{vmatrix}\begin{matrix} A & K \\ D & L \\ G & M \end{matrix}}{\begin{vmatrix} A & B & C \\ D & E & F \\ G & H & J \end{vmatrix}\begin{matrix} A & B \\ D & E \\ G & H \end{matrix}} = \frac{ALJ + KFG + CDM - GLC - MFA - JDK}{AEJ + BFG + CDH - GEC - HFA - JDB}$$

$$Z = \frac{\begin{vmatrix} A & B & K \\ D & E & L \\ G & H & M \end{vmatrix}\begin{matrix} A & B \\ D & E \\ G & H \end{matrix}}{\begin{vmatrix} A & B & C \\ D & E & F \\ G & H & J \end{vmatrix}\begin{matrix} A & B \\ D & E \\ G & H \end{matrix}} = \frac{AEM + BLG + KDH - GEK - HLA - MDB}{AEJ + BFG + CDH - GEC - HFA - JDB}$$

Example 7

Use Cramer's Rule to solve this system of equations.

$$3X + 2Y + 4Z = 9 \qquad 4X + 3Y - 2Z = 6 \qquad 5X + 4Y - 3Z = 8$$

$$X = \frac{\begin{vmatrix} 9 & 2 & 4 \\ 6 & 3 & -2 \\ 8 & 4 & -3 \end{vmatrix} \begin{matrix} 9 & 2 \\ 6 & 3 \\ 8 & 4 \end{matrix}}{\begin{vmatrix} 3 & 2 & 4 \\ 4 & 3 & -2 \\ 5 & 4 & -3 \end{vmatrix} \begin{matrix} 3 & 2 \\ 4 & 3 \\ 5 & 4 \end{matrix}} = \frac{(9)(3)(-3) + (2)(-2)(8) + (4)(6)(4) - (8)(3)(4) - (4)(-2)(9) - (-3)(6)(2)}{(3)(3)(-3) + (2)(-2)(5) + (4)(4)(4) - (5)(3)(4) - (4)(-2)(3) - (-3)(4)(2)} =$$

$$\frac{(-81) + (-32) + (96) - (96) - (-72) - (-36)}{(-27) + (-20) + (64) - (60) - (-24) - (-24)} = \frac{-5}{+5} = -1$$

$$Y = \frac{\begin{vmatrix} 3 & 9 & 4 \\ 4 & 6 & -2 \\ 5 & 8 & -3 \end{vmatrix} \begin{matrix} 3 & 9 \\ 4 & 6 \\ 5 & 8 \end{matrix}}{\begin{vmatrix} 3 & 2 & 4 \\ 4 & 3 & -2 \\ 5 & 4 & -3 \end{vmatrix} \begin{matrix} 3 & 2 \\ 4 & 3 \\ 5 & 4 \end{matrix}} = \frac{(3)(6)(-3) + (9)(-2)(5) + (4)(4)(8) - (5)(6)(4) - (8)(-2)(3) - (-3)(4)(9)}{(3)(3)(-3) + (2)(-2)(5) + (4)(4)(4) - (5)(3)(4) - (4)(-2)(3) - (-3)(4)(2)} =$$

$$\frac{(-54) + (-90) + (128) - (120) - (-48) - (-108)}{(-27) + (-20) + (64) - (60) - (-24) - (-24)} = \frac{20}{5} = 4$$

$$Z = \frac{\begin{vmatrix} 3 & 2 & 9 \\ 4 & 3 & 6 \\ 5 & 4 & 8 \end{vmatrix} \begin{matrix} 3 & 2 \\ 4 & 3 \\ 5 & 4 \end{matrix}}{\begin{vmatrix} 3 & 2 & 4 \\ 4 & 3 & -2 \\ 5 & 4 & -3 \end{vmatrix} \begin{matrix} 3 & 2 \\ 4 & 3 \\ 5 & 4 \end{matrix}} = \frac{(3)(3)(8) + (2)(6)(5) + (9)(4)(4) - (5)(3)(9) - (4)(6)(3) - (8)(4)(2)}{(3)(3)(-3) + (2)(-2)(5) + (4)(4)(4) - (5)(3)(4) - (4)(-2)(3) - (-3)(4)(2)} =$$

$$\frac{(72) + (60) + (144) - (135) - (72) - (64)}{(-27) + (-20) + (64) - (60) - (-24) - (-24)} = \frac{5}{5} = 1$$

Solution: (X, Y, Z) = (-1, 4, 1)

4. Use Cramer's Rule to solve the system of equations.

$$5X - 3Y + 3Z = 3 \qquad 2X - 6Y - 4Z = 2 \qquad 3X - 5Y + Z = -3$$

Symbols & Tables

SYMBOLS

$<$	less than
$>$	greater than
$\leq$	less than or equal to
$\geq$	greater than or equal to
$=$	equal in numerical value
$\neq$	not equal to
$\approx$	approximately equal
%	percent
$\vert\ \vert$	absolute value
$\sqrt{}$	square root
Δ	change in

FACTORING

$$(A + B)^2 = A^2 + 2AB + B^2$$
$$(A - B)^2 = A^2 - 2AB + B^2$$
$$(A + B)^3 = A^3 + 3A^2B + 3AB^2 + B^3$$
$$(A - B)^3 = A^3 - 3A^2B + 3AB^2 - B^3$$

QUADRATIC FORMULA

$$X = \frac{-B \pm \sqrt{B^2 - 4AC}}{2A}$$

MIDPOINT FORMULA

$$\frac{X_1 + X_2}{2}, \frac{Y_1 + Y_2}{2}$$

PYTHAGOREAN THEOREM

$$L^2 + L^2 = H^2$$

DISTANCE FORMULA

$$D^2 = \Delta X^2 + \Delta Y^2 \text{ or } D = \sqrt{\Delta X^2 + \Delta Y^2}$$

IMPERIAL TO METRIC

1 inch $\approx$ 2.5 centimeters

1 yard (36") $\approx$ .9 meters

1 mile $\approx$ 1.6 kilometers

1 ounce $\approx$ 28 grams

1 pound $\approx$ .45 kilograms

1 quart $\approx$ .95 liters

METRIC TO IMPERIAL

1 centimeter $\approx$ .4 inches

1 meter (39.37") $\approx$ 1.1 yards

1 kilometer $\approx$ .62 miles

1 gram $\approx$ .035 ounces

1 kilogram $\approx$ 2.2 pounds

1 liter $\approx$ 1.06 quarts

SLOPE OF A LINE

$$\text{slope} = \frac{\text{up}}{\text{over}} = \frac{Y_2 - Y_1}{X_2 - X_1}$$

DISCRIMINANT

$$b^2 - 4ac$$

AXIS OF SYMMETRY OF A PARABOLA

$$X = \frac{-B}{2A}$$

SLOPE-INTERCEPT FORM

$$Y = mX + b$$

EQUATION OF A:

line	$AX + BY = C$
circle	$AX^2 + AY^2 = C$
ellipse	$AX^2 + BY^2 = C$
parabola	$Y = X^2$
hyperbola	$XY = C$ and $X^2 - Y^2 = C$

ORDER OF OPERATIONS

Parachute Expert My Dear Aunt Sally

1. Parentheses
2. Exponents
3. Multiplication and Division
4. Addition and Subtraction

BINOMIAL THEOREM

$$(A - B)^N = A^N B^0 + \frac{N}{1} A^{N-1} B^1 + \frac{N(N-1)}{1(2)} A^{N-2} B^2 + \frac{N(N-1)(N-2)}{1(2)(3)} A^{N-3} B^3 \ldots A^0 B^N$$

ATOMIC WEIGHT TABLE

Symbol	Element	Atomic Weight	Symbol	Element	Atomic Weight
H	Hydrogen	1	Mg	Magnesium	24
Li	Lithium	7	Si	Silicon	28
Be	Beryllium	9	P	Phosphorus	31
B	Boron	11	S	Sulfur	32
C	Carbon	12	Cl	Chlorine	35
N	Nitrogen	14	K	Potassium	39
O	Oxygen	16	Ca	Calcium	40
F	Fluorine	19	Cr	Chromium	52
Na	Sodium	23	Fe	Iron	56

Basic Algebra Review
for Math-U-See Algebra 2

Math-U-See *Algebra 2* assumes a solid understanding of math concepts taught in *Algebra 1* and *Pre-Algebra*. However, we recognize that students may need to be reminded of what they have learned.

The following summary is designed to help a student "warm up" for *Algebra 2*. Hopefully each concept will be familiar to the student. If a concept listed here is confusing or unfamiliar, we strongly recommend reviewing it before beginning *Algebra 2*. You may use the "Secondary Levels Master Index" near the end of your instruction manual to find which previous level introduced a particular concept.

Some concepts, such as graphing and coin problems, are re-taught in detail in *Algebra 2*, and so are not included in this review.

Absolute Value
Absolute value lines make the value between them positive.

$$|3 + 5| = |8| = 8$$
$$|3 - 5| = |-2| = 2$$

Associative Property
When adding or multiplying, numbers may be grouped differently without affecting the answer. This property does not work for subtraction or division.

$$(3 + 4) + 2 = 3 + (4 + 2) = 9$$
$$(3 \times A) \times B = 3 \times (A \times B) = 3AB$$

Commutative Property
When adding or multiplying, the order of numbers may be changed without affecting the answer. This property does not work for subtraction or division.

$$2A + 5A = 5A + 2A = 7A$$
$$B \times A \times 6 = 6 \times A \times B = (6)(A)(B) = 6AB$$

Distributive Property

A common factor may be multiplied across all the terms of an expression.

$$4(3 + 4X - 2Y) = (4)(3) + (4)(4X) - (4)(2Y) = 12 + 16X - 8Y$$
$$-X(2 - 6Y) = (-X)(2) - (-X)(6Y) = -2X + 6XY$$

Exponents

An exponent indicates fast multiplying of the same number. Operations with exponents are reviewed in lesson 1.

$$3^2 = 3 \times 3 = 9$$

$$(3X)^3 = (3X)(3X)(3X) = 27X^3$$

$$(-3)^2 = (-3)(-3) = 9 \qquad -3^2 = -(3)(3) = -9$$

$$\left(\frac{2}{3}\right)^2 = \frac{4}{9}$$

Fractions

Fractions with unknowns are handled according to the same rules as numerical fractions. Keep in mind that a fraction is another way of writing a division problem.

Greatest Common Factor (GCF)

This is the largest number that will divide evenly into two or more factors.

The GCF of 28 and 35 is 7.
The GCF of 4X and $2X^2Y$ is 2X.

Least Common Multiple (LCM)

This is the smallest number that is a multiple of two or more numbers.

The LCM of 10 and 100 is 100.
The LCM of 5Y, 10Y, and 25 is 50Y.

Negative Numbers

Operations with negative numbers follow these rules.

Addition	$(-4) + (-5) = -9$	$(+4) + (-5) = -1$
		$(-4) + (+5) = 1$
Subtraction	$(-9) - (+5) = -14$	$9 - 5 = 4$
		$(-9) - (-5) = (-9) + 5 = -4$
Multiplication	$(-3)(4) = -12$	$(-3)(-4) = 12$
Division	$(-12) \div (-3) = 4$	$(-12) \div (3) = -4$

Order of Operations

When simplifying an equation, operations must be done in the following order: parentheses, exponents, multiplication and division, addition and subtraction. Multiplication and division are done together left to right across the problem as they occur. The same is true for addition and subtraction.

Radicals

The radical sign indicates the square root of a number. A perfect square has a whole number square root. The square roots of many other numbers are irrational numbers. Operations with radicals are reviewed in lesson 4.

$$\sqrt{4} = 2$$

$$\sqrt{x^2} = x$$

$$\sqrt{2} = 1.4142...$$

Solving for an Unknown

There is often more than one way to solve an equation. The basic principle is that any operation may be done to an equation as long as the same thing is done to both sides.

Terms

The terms in an algebra problem are separated by addition or subtraction signs. They may not be combined unless they have the same value. Values within terms are being multiplied by each other. Study the examples.

$2A + 4A = 6A$

Note that $6A = (6)(A) = 6 \times A = 6 \cdot A$.

$2X + 4Y = 2X + 4Y$

X and Y are different values,
so the terms cannot be combined.

$5X^3 + 3X^3 = 8X^3$

X^3 and X^3 are the same value,
so the terms can be combined.

$5AX^2 + 3AX^2 = 8AX^2$

AX^2 and AX^2 are the same value,
so the terms can be combined.

$5AX^2 + 3AX^3 = 5AX^2 + 3AX^3$

AX^2 and AX^3 are different values,
so the terms cannot be combined.

Glossary

A–D

absolute value - the value of a number without its sign, or the difference between a number and zero expressed as a positive number

algebra - a branch of mathematics that deals with numbers, which may be represented by letters or symbols

asymptote - a line that is continually approached by a given curve but is never met by that curve

base - a particular side or face of a geometric figure used to calculate area or volume; a number that is raised to a power; the number that is the foundation in a given number system

binomial - an algebraic expression with two terms

binomial theorem - a formula for finding the complete expansion of any positive power of a binomial

coefficient - a quantity placed before and multiplying the variable in an algebraic expression

completing the square - a technique for solving a quadratic equation that involves rewriting it as a perfect square plus a constant

complex number - a combination of a real and an imaginary number in the form $a + bi$

cone - a solid with a circular base and a curved surface that rises to a point

conic section - a curve that results when a cone is intersected by a plane

conjugate - a binomial formed by negating the second term of a given binomial

constant - a fixed, unchanging value

difference of two squares - an expression in which one squared number is subtracted from another squared number

E–I

ellipse - a regular oval created by moving a point around two foci

empty set - a set having no elements; also called *null set*

hyperbola - a conic section that forms two congruent open curves facing in opposite directions on a graph

imaginary number - a number that, when squared, gives a negative product; generally written in the form bi, where i equals the square root of -1

integer - a non-fractional number that can be positive, negative, or zero

irrational numbers - numbers that cannot be written as fractions and form non-repeating, non-terminating decimals

L–O

linear equation - an equation that creates a straight line when graphed

magnitude - length of a vector

maximum - the greatest value of a function at a particular point in its domain; plural is *maxima*

minimum - the least value of a function at a particular point in its domain; plural is *minima*

multiplicative inverse - the number that, when multiplied by a given number, has a product of 1; also called *reciprocal*

natural numbers - whole numbers from 1 to infinity; also called *counting numbers*

origin - on a coordinate grid, the point at the intersection of the axes, generally identified by the ordered pair (0, 0)

P–Q

parabola - a conic section that forms a symmetrical curve on a graph

parallel lines - lines in the same plane that do not intersect

Pascal's triangle - a triangular array of numbers that has a variety of mathematical applications

perfect cube - a number that has a whole number as its cube root

perfect square - a number that has a whole number as its square root

polynomial - an algebraic expression with more than one term

quadratic equation - an equation where the highest power of the variable is 2

quadratic expression - an expression where the highest power of the variable is 2

R–S

radical - an expression containing a root

ratio - the relationship between two values; can be written in fractional form

rational expression - an expression that is the ratio of two polynomials

rational numbers - numbers that can be written as ratios or fractions, including decimals

real numbers - numbers that can be written as decimals, including rational and irrational numbers

reciprocal - the number that, when multiplied by a given number, has a product of 1; also called *multiplicative inverse*

resultant vector - the combination of two or more vectors

scientific notation - a way to write numbers using the product of a base and a power of ten

significant digits - digits that indicate the accuracy of a measurement

simultaneous equations - a pair of equations with two unknown variables that must be solved at the same time

T–Z

trinomial - an algebraic expression with three terms

unknown - a specific quantity that has not yet been determined

variable - a value that is not fixed or determined, often representing a range of possible values

vector - a quantity with both direction and magnitude

vertex - the highest or lowest point of a parabola; the endpoint shared by two rays, line segments, or edges; plural is *vertices*